The Latest Vegan Type 2 Diabetic Diet Cookbook for Newly Diagnosed

1000 Days of Tasty, Delicious, Low-Sugar, Low-Carb Plant-Based Recipes for Blood Sugar Management and Control + 30 Days Meal Plan

Charlotte N. Smith

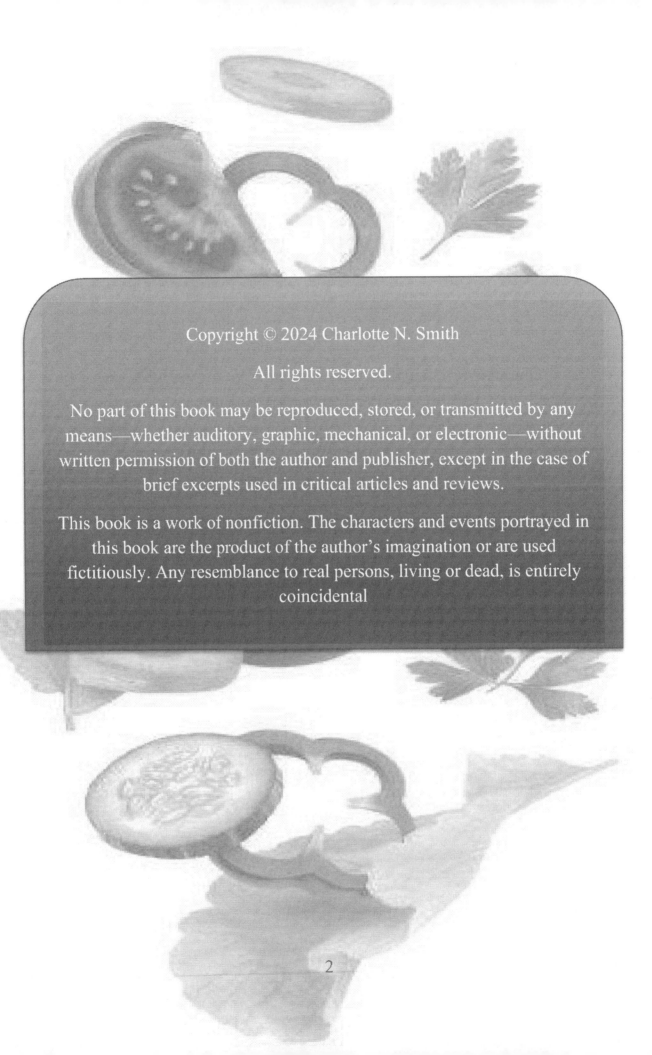

TABLET OF CONTENT

INTRODUCTION

There are many ways to help, prevent, or manage type 2 diabetes. Exercise and physical activity significantly improve the body's ability to use insulin, thus an essential factor in controlling type 2 diabetes. Both aerobic exercise and resistance training are helpful. Medications and insulin therapy are often used to treat type 2 diabetes, but they come with adverse side effects, frequently leading to the worsening of the initial problem. This is why it is vital to find other ways to impact type 2 diabetes positively. One such way is with a vegan diet.

Type 2 diabetes is a lifestyle disease that is on the rise. As we have become a more sedentary society, unhealthy eating practices have led to this growing epidemic. Diabetes is a disease in which the body does not produce or properly use insulin. Insulin is a hormone needed to convert sugar, starches, and other food into energy needed for daily life.

The cause of type 2 diabetes is an excess accumulation of sugar in the blood, often associated with an insufficient conversion of sugar to energy. It is as if the body's leading fuel source has become a thick, sticky syrup. People with diabetes are at greater risk of heart disease, stroke, high blood pressure, blindness, kidney disease, and amputations. An estimated 10.5 million Americans are at risk for developing type 2 diabetes, and the numbers are increasing rapidly.

Understanding Type 2 Diabetes

Diabetes is a severe medical condition characterized by the body's inadequacy to regulate insulin, which leads to substantially high blood sugar levels. The raised blood sugar levels can cause damage to the nerves, retinas, blood vessels, and kidneys. In diabetes, there is an increased risk of atherosclerosis. In this condition, harmful fatty deposits get laid down on the insides of the arteries, causing them to thicken and constrict more than usual. It increases the risk of heart attacks, stroke, and poor circulation in the extremities. Too high or too low blood glucose levels can be a sign of the onset of diabetes or a diagnosing factor of diabetes.

Typically, the body can regulate and stabilize glucose concentration in the blood. This is partially controlled by the hormone insulin, produced by the pancreas to facilitate the entry of glucose from the blood into the cells, where it is used as fuel. Suppose glucose levels rise too high, perhaps after a meal, and more glucose is present than the cells need. In that case, the pancreas produces more insulin to enable increased glucose uptake by the cells and to store the excess glucose as glycogen in the liver. If glucose levels fall between meals or during physical exertion, insulin release is reduced, which means less glucose is utilized by the cells. More is liberated from glycogen stores in the liver to maintain a stable blood glucose level. In diabetes, this control mechanism is impaired.

Benefits of a Vegan Diet for Type 2 Diabetics management

The study found that a low-fat vegan diet does improve glycemic control in individuals with type II diabetes. The diet appears to have a dramatic effect on A1c, potentially achieving a level lower than that often seen with medication. It may also be beneficial for reducing diabetes medication use.

The results were found by assessing the changes in haemoglobin A1c and utilizing ANCOVA analysis of the difference from baseline to 22 weeks. Participants in the plant-based diet group could also reduce haemoglobin A1c more effectively than medication. It led to a similar study with 86,000 AHS-2 cohort participants and an 8-year follow-up. In addition, an EDIP investigation occurred in 11,679 AHS-2 participants.

The study was conducted and published by the Journal of Diabetes Care. The study aimed to compare a low-fat plant-based vegan diet to the American Diabetes Association recommended diet by assessing glycemic control and risk factors for cardiovascular disease in people with type II diabetes. It was a prospective randomized study that was 22 weeks in duration with 99 participants with type II diabetes. The participants were 30-70 years old, and the average BMI was 34.5 kg/m2. They were primarily recruited from the diabetes education programs of the University of North Carolina and people in the surrounding community.

The diet was to be prepared and consumed at home and in an amount that maintained their body weight. The participants were asked to make no changes in exercise and to keep medication use constant during the study. Compliance with the diet was monitored with weekly dietary logs, and both groups were instructed to test urinary ketones daily. Changes in medications would occur if participants' blood glucose or urinary ketones suggested a need for change.

The vegan group received a weekly visit from a study dietitian, and the AHA group was encouraged to meet with the study dietitian on weeks 1, 3, 12, and 18. Beyond these general study outlines, the study was divided into two phases. An initial 5-week period of randomization to the new diet and a second 17-week period of diabetes and CVD risk factor assessment. Subsequent follow-up studies have occurred to gauge the long-term effects.

People have a large variety of foods they can eat while dealing with type II diabetes and making sure that it is healthy is very important. Many diets are recommended for diabetics, such as the American Diabetes Association diet, the Mediterranean diet, and the vegetarian diet. A study now shows that a vegan diet, or a diet that eliminates all animal products, can be very beneficial for type II diabetics. It is important because although there are many dietary options, not all are effective for lowering blood glucose levels, and not all are safe for diabetics in the long term.

How This Cookbook Can Help

Understanding how this cookbook can help you. As soon as you begin reading through this cookbook, you will experience a change in how you consume food. The pages are filled with information on how to adopt a vegan diet and effectively manage your diabetes. This book provides clear and simple steps to introduce changes to your dietary habits. Most readers today do not have the time to research an individual topic and find solutions.

My goal is to provide the information for you, offering guidance and support every step of the way. If you'd like to fully understand the impact of a vegan diet on diabetes and how to adopt this way of living, there is no doubt that this book is for you. This book is also suitable for anyone who has a family member or friend with diabetes. By supporting a change in their diet, these recipes can provide a tasty alternative to the typical low-fat, high-carbohydrate vegan meals and significantly improve their diabetes management.

Last of all, this book can help new and even long-term vegans who are not managing their diabetes well but do not wish to adopt another way of eating. I hope to show them that diabetes can be managed on a vegan diet, and this book provides the tools to do so. So, how can this book help you? This book is an effective tool to help you learn and adopt a vegan diet if you are a diabetic, type 1 or 2, requiring a healthier way of eating for better diabetes management.

The introduction is a simple and clear explanation of the reasons for a vegan diet and its benefits on diabetes, giving readers an understanding of how and why a vegan diet may help. The recipes and meal plan in this 4-week kick-start program are the practical tools to implement this way of eating. All recipes have consistent carbohydrates and exchanges per serving to help you achieve glycemic control. A structured meal plan will assist in planning your food choices and management of medication. The shopping lists for each week will make it easy to prepare well for the week ahead.

If you have a long-term way of eating that you are satisfied with, you can use the recipes in this book. You will benefit from a nutritional analysis of each recipe showing the % daily intake for macronutrients and vitamin and mineral content. It enables you to know the quality of the food you are eating and can be helpful for specific dietary changes to accomplish better health.

Getting Started with a Vegan Type 2 Diabetic Diet

If you are new to veganism, the change can be difficult. Someone who is newly diagnosed with diabetes may find the struggle to be even greater. It almost feels like your favourite foods have been burgers, steaks, and fried chicken are no longer allowed. Prepare yourself for the change; don't dive headfirst into the new diet.

Start by eating more meat substitutes such as veggie burgers, soy-based hot dogs, and seitan. Over time, phase out the products with high-fat content and introduce more beans, lentils, and tofu into your diet. You can then introduce nuts, seeds, and other healthy fats from those types of food. Another tip for making the transition more manageable is to "veganize" your favourite non-vegan meals. You might have to experiment in the kitchen with recipes or look online for vegan recipes, but there are many ways to make a vegan version of your favourite meal.

You can find countless cookbooks with recipes for vegan macaroni and cheese, lasagna, and other comfort foods. Making a vegan version of a non-vegan meal can satisfy your cravings. Since these vegan meals are sure to be healthier than their non-vegan counterparts, a diabetic should have no problem indulging in a modest portion.

Transitioning to a Vegan Lifestyle

Making any lifestyle change can be difficult. The same goes for individuals making the transition to a vegan diet. Whether due to health concerns, environmental implications, or the welfare of animals, people find many reasons to try a vegan diet. Making the transition in small steps can be the key to creating a lasting change.

There are no strict dietary limitations; stepping stones can make the process less overwhelming. Set the pace by incorporating faux meat and dairy alternatives. It can make the transition nearly seamless. Convenience foods such as frozen vegan entrees can also be helpful, especially in the initial phases. Try incorporating more leafy green vegetables and whole grain products. These foods are foundational in the vegan diet and can be great staples. Look up a few recipes and slowly build a collection of quick, easy meals.

This will prevent getting stuck in a rut with the same boring salads. Changing the ways you eat can be an interesting and exciting experiment. With a wide variety of vegan recipes and foods available, you can try something new each day for weeks and never have to eat the same thing. This variety can keep a vegan diet from getting boring. Most importantly, remember that it's not about being perfect. Don't let a slip-up make you feel like a failure. Just start fresh from your very next meal and move on. By choosing a vegan meal, you are furthering your cause by a large margin. It can be beneficial for diabetics, considering the benefits a vegan diet can offer to their condition.

Essential Nutrients for Type 2 Diabetics

As the only negatively viewed nutrient, vitamin B12 can be obtained from fortified foods and B12 supplements. Moderate sun exposure and vitamin D supplements are safe and effective for vitamin D. Consuming algae-derived omega-3 supplements is a sound and secure way to obtain essential long-chain omega-3s. It is possible to get iodine from foods grown in iodine-rich soil. Iodine supplements should be cautiously used, as intakes greater than 1700mcg daily can be harmful. Iron can be found in legumes, tofu, seeds, and dried fruits. Enhancing the absorption of plant iron by consuming it with a source of vitamin C is an excellent way to obtain iron.

However, iron supplements may be needed if you are anaemic. Since dairy products are low in lactose, calcium from fortified non-dairy drinks is an excellent alternative to calcium supplements. For zinc, consuming a variety of foods high in zinc is sufficient to avoid supplements.

First and foremost, when considering a vegan diet, it is crucial to know how to consume various essential nutrients and vitamins derived from a vegan lifestyle. The primary nutrients of concern are vitamin B12, vitamin D, long-chain omega-3s, iodine, iron, calcium, and zinc. These nutrients can be obtained from both plant and animal sources.

When considering vitamins and minerals, it is possible to obtain all the needed nutrients through diet alone by consuming a wide variety of foods and being mindful to include certain fortified foods. Taking a multivitamin can help with nutrient balance and may be beneficial in the long run. Consulting with a registered dietitian for personalized guidance is ideal.

Blood Sugar Management Through Diet

Blood sugar management facts: The food that people eat is broken down into simple sugars, primarily glucose. Insulin is required for glucose to enter the cells. However, in diabetic people, possessing an insufficient supply of insulin or an ineffectual use of insulin causes the glucose concentration in the blood to rise.

Diabetic people are striving to keep their blood glucose levels down as close to normal as possible. A significant part of managing blood glucose levels is consuming a healthy diet. When people hear 'diet', they think it is just about losing weight. However, that is the wrong concept. Diet is the sum of food consumed by a person. It is not the short-term solution of eating less food to try and lose weight. It is changing those eating behaviours for a lifetime. The first step in evolving dietary behaviours is understanding what constitutes a healthy diet.

There is so much confusion regarding what a healthy diet for a diabetic person is. It is due to the bombardment of so-called 'diabetic food' or 'products suitable for diabetics' on consumers. The general idea of healthy eating is similar for everyone, so a diet that is good for an average person will also be suitable for a diabetic person. This contradicts the belief that a healthy diet is more expensive and that going on a short-term diet with drastic changes will control diabetes.

It is a healthy diet which will benefit a diabetic, and it is diet control, such as reducing the intake of sugar and fat, which should also be the objective for weight control. A diabetic does not have to avoid a specific type of food; with a balanced meal plan, they can incorporate a small number of sweets into their diet. A healthy meal plan for a diabetic is low in saturated and trans-fat moderate in salt and sugar, with meals based on whole grains, vegetables, and fruits. It is best to consult a dietitian for a more specific meal plan to suit individual needs.

Preparing Your Kitchen and Pantry

With that all said, here are your necessities when stocking your kitchen:

Juices and sodas often have extended shelf lives due to added preservatives. Try to find all-natural juice; if the expiration date is six months away, there's a good chance it's not purely natural! The same goes for canned fruits and veggies. They are often loaded with syrups and sugars. Find frozen or fresh items, which is sometimes better than fresh, considering it's picked and packed at the season's peak.

As for the multitudes of dairy products, there is a selection of rice and soy versions. You can find rice, soy, and almond milk, which all have non-dairy substitutes for yogurt and ice cream. When looking for cereals and bread, check the health food aisle for organic products with lower sugar and higher fibre content.

As mentioned earlier, there is a big difference between vegetarian and vegan. As a vegan, there are no animal products in your diet, so you will have to be a master of reading labels. There are often "hidden" animal products such as whey, casein, or albumin, so don't take the term vegan at face value. The positive is there are plenty of substitutes for these, all of which can be found at various health food stores and many grocers. Try using tofu, tempeh, soy cheese, etc.

As a diabetic embarking on a new journey, you must always have supplies and ingredients on hand. Keep in mind that this is different than any typical "diet". This is a lifestyle change, and you will create new routines and new habits. Make sure you have the necessities, and remember that it will involve a little investment at first, but nothing will compare to your health.

container, and an efficient handheld citrus juicer. A steamer is essential for those looking to minimize added oil in their diet and cook vegetables to maintain their nutrient content best. A silicone steam basket is simple and more friendly on your wallet. A slow cooker is an easy way to make large portions of soups or stews with minimal effort and time.

These are an excellent alternative for days when you are too busy to cook at the end of a long day. A high-quality knife or knife set is also precious. A sharp, quality knife can make chopping vegetables simple and pleasant. For those looking to cut grain from their diet, a spiralizer is an easy-to-use tool that can turn many vegetables into fun noodle shapes. When reading ingredient labels, avoiding products with ingredients you can't pronounce, do not know, or are clearly labelled as an unnecessary, unhealthy substance is ideal. Commonly avoided ingredients include artificial sweeteners, high fructose corn syrup, artificial colours, and preservatives.

Essential tools, pantry staples, and how to read food labels.

Essential tools vary and range from a blender, particularly a high-speed blender, to speed up the mixing process and make smooth soups and smoothies to a food processor, which is very useful for evenly chopping vegetables, a food storage

14

Try to purchase predominantly whole ingredients and avoid items with a long list of multiple preservatives. Products with a single ingredient are the best, including raw nuts and seeds or bags of legumes.

Meal Planning, Portion Control and Prepping Tips

Meal planning techniques can be adapted to include daily lunches prepared the night before and quick-to-prepare breakfast options. The aim is to eliminate the desire to purchase prepared foods or dine out by always ensuring that a healthier, home-cooked alternative is readily available.

You can begin compiling a small stockpile of frozen dinners by always cooking more significant portions of your meals and freezing the leftovers. This becomes especially useful when there is minimal time to cook. Preparing and freezing meals can also be a saviour when you are too tired or uninterested to cook and are considering take-out. In this case, fast food can be replaced by a pre-prepared frozen meal, which requires reheating.

Beginning a meal plan can be as simple as writing down what you plan to eat next week. This can be made more accessible by noting down a daily menu on the Vegan type 2 Diabetics Meal Planning Worksheet included within this guide. After a week or two of noting down your planned meals, the next step is to create a system of menus that can be rotated weekly. This system should aim to be somewhat flexible to allow for impromptu social events or changes in daily routine.

Fitness pros will tell you that grocery shopping and preparing your meals are the best ways to take control of your dietary life and promote healthy eating. Conversely, poorly managed meal planning and prep can lead to unhealthy food choices and impulsive eating, a temptation worth avoiding once thoroughly understood.

Developing a strategic meal plan is crucial to maintaining and controlling your blood sugar levels. It does not necessarily indicate that one must eat restrictive, bland foods. It means that you should have healthier food choices readily available. If your meals are usually unstructured, and you eat at random times throughout the day, implementing a meal plan can significantly improve your eating habits.

Grocery Shopping List for a Vegan Type 2 Diabetic Diet

Before purchasing food, consider checking the nutrient and glycemic index. High glycemic index foods can cause blood sugar levels to rise too high. High GI is >70, medium GI is 56-69, and low GI is <55. For example, if you find rice with a GI of 80, you can opt for low GI foods such as basmati rice with a GI of 58 or Jasmine rice with a GI of 50 to lower blood sugar spikes. Always read food labels when shopping and avoid foods with high sugar or added syrup. Choose fresh or frozen vegetables and fruits without sauce, syrup, or ready-to-eat meals. Lastly, choose canned fruits in natural juice and unsweetened apple sauce.

Creating a meal plan using the foods you purchase is essential, as meal planning can save time, money, and effort. The amount of each food to buy depends on the meal plan. Ensure that you have enough nutrients, fibre, and energy. Regular physical activity can improve blood glucose levels and overall health. Refer to the examples of foods and the required nutrients and fibre.

Remember, a vegan type 2 diabetic diet is high in carbohydrates and fibre. Carbohydrates are digested and can increase blood sugar levels, while fibre can slow down and prevent blood sugar spikes. It is beneficial for preventing blood sugar levels from rising too high. Examples of carbohydrate-based foods and fruits include brown rice, whole-meal bread, homemade oats, and any fruit. When choosing fruits, opt for fresh ones. Canned fruits are acceptable, but choose those in natural juice and avoid dried fruits.

Managing Type 2 Diabetes Through Lifestyle Changes

When dealing with Type 2 Diabetes, weight management is crucial. Being overweight is the single leading cause of type 2 diabetes. Being 10 to 20 pounds overweight increases the risk of getting diabetes. It is not fully understood what causes type 2 diabetes, but it is known that being overweight is a primary cause. It's believed that being overweight puts stress on the insulating cells and can hinder the glucose metabolism process. Also, being overweight can cause insulin resistance in the body, which is a significant factor in the development of type 2 diabetes.

Insulin resistance occurs in very few individuals with a healthy weight but occurs in up to 85% of overweight people. High insulin resistance leads to the need for high levels of insulin to control glucose levels, and eventually, insulin production cannot increase. 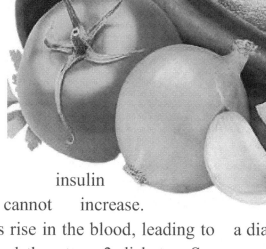 Glucose levels rise in the blood, leading to pre-diabetes and then type 2 diabetes. So, the only way to end insulin resistance and prevent causing further damage to your body is to lose weight and take the stress off the insulating cells. It can be done through regular physical activity and dieting.

Having diabetes requires you to make changes in your life. Unfortunately, virtually all Americans lead unhealthy lifestyles, so making healthy changes is easier said than done. At the same time, it is more of an issue for those with diabetes because making healthy changes can mean having lower blood sugar, blood pressure, and cholesterol levels - leading to a longer, healthier life. Although changing your lifestyle might take some time, doing so has definite benefits.

In the Diabetes Prevention Program, an extensive study of people at high risk for diabetes, those who lost a small amount of weight and changed the amount of walking they did lowered their chances of developing diabetes by 58%. It was true for the age groups, but surprisingly, the people who benefited the most were those over 60. Why wait for a diagnosis? Make the change now!

Regular Physical Activity and Exercise

Before beginning any exercise program, it is essential to talk to your doctor. It is crucial if you have not been active, if you are overweight, or if you have heart disease, high blood pressure, high cholesterol, tobacco use, or if you are over 35. He may want a fitness assessment and an electrocardiogram (ECG). It assesses whether you have any limits on what you can do safely. If you are at high risk of a heart attack or you have heart disease, your doctor may want to do an exercise stress test. This test involves making ECG recordings before, during, and after exercise, often combined with blood pressure measurements.

Try to make activity part of your everyday life. It's easier to make activity a habit if you integrate it into your daily routine. Vary activities so you don't get bored. For the activity to be beneficial, you must do it for at least 30 minutes 5 days a week. The 30 minutes can be split up into smaller 10-minute sessions.

Increasing physical activity is essential to any type 2 diabetic management plan. It does not need to involve joining a gym and going through a strenuous workout. Choosing an activity or range of activities, that are enjoyable will aid compliance. Exercise should be a mixture of aerobic activity and strength training. Aerobic activity is the activity that makes you breathe hard and sweat. It can make your heart and blood vessels healthier. Strength training makes your muscles stronger. This helps the muscles take up more blood sugar. It also helps the muscles use the blood sugar for energy.

Stress Management Techniques

It is a fact that stress has a substantial direct influence on bodily functions. Significant life-altering decisions need to be made immediately upon being diagnosed. It is usual for individuals to feel overwhelmed in a heightened emotional state. Since depression is common in diabetics, it is imperative to seek help if any of these feelings persist. Learn relaxation techniques such as deep breathing, meditation, yoga, massage, and so on that can help you relax physically and mentally. Schedule time for laughter and socializing with friends. In the long run, it is essential to identify stressors in your life, slowly develop a feasible plan to eliminate as many stressors as possible and learn to cope with inevitable ones.

Combining these methods can help lower stress hormones and blood sugars, ultimately improving diabetes management. Take a few minutes to read "Diabetes and Me" to analyze your feelings and obtain a positive attitude about diabetes.

Monitoring Blood Sugar Levels

Insulin and certain diabetes medications can cause your blood sugar to drop too low. Plan to have the following supplies ready for treating low blood sugar available at all times: table sugar dissolved in water, fruit juice, regular (not diet) soda, popcorn, raisins, hard candy, jelly beans or gumdrops, glucose tablets.

Your blood sugar might be too high or too low if you are experiencing the following symptoms: High blood sugar, Increased thirst and urination, increased hunger, blurred vision, and fatigue. Low blood sugar: Shaking or trembling, rapid heart rate, sweating, anxiety, dizziness.

Test your blood sugar level whenever you suspect it might be too high or too low. Usually, you will test your blood sugar before meals and occasionally after eating. You should also test before, during, and after exercise. Testing more often can provide valuable information to help with your blood sugar management. If you are ill and not eating, you should still test your blood sugar regularly. If you're taking medications that can cause low blood sugar reactions, you should test before driving and before potentially hazardous activities such as operating heavy machinery.

BREAKFAST

Super-fast Scrambled Tofu

Prep. Time: 5 mins **cooking time**: 10 mins **Servings:** 2

Ingredients:

- 1 tablespoon olive oil
- 1 block (about 14 oz) extra-firm tofu, drained and crumbled
- 1/4 cup nutritional yeast
- 1/2 teaspoon ground turmeric
- 1/2 teaspoon garlic powder
- Salt, to taste

- Freshly ground black pepper, to taste
- Fresh parsley for garnish

Preparation Method:

1. Heat the olive oil in a skillet over medium heat. Add scrambled tofu and cook for 3-4 minutes, stirring occasionally.

2. Sprinkle nutritional yeast, ground turmeric, and garlic powder over the tofu. Stir well to coat evenly.

3. Continue cooking for 3-4 minutes or until the tofu is heated and slightly crispy.

4. Season with salt and black pepper to taste. Garnish with fresh parsley before serving

Nutritional Information: Calories: 200 kcal Carbohydrates: 5g Protein: 15g Fat 13g Fiber: 2g

Super Green Superfruit Protein Smoothie

Preparation Time:5 minutes **cooking time:**0 minutes (This recipe is prepared cold)
Servings: 1

Ingredients:

- 1 cup fresh spinach
- 1/2 cup kale leaves, stems removed
- 1/2 cup frozen mixed berries
- 1/2 banana, frozen
- 1 tablespoon chia seeds
- 1 tablespoon hemp seeds
- 1 scoop vegan protein powder
- 1 cup unsweetened almond milk (or any unsweetened plant-based milk)
- Ice cubes (optional)

Preparation Method:

1. combine fresh spinach, kale leaves, frozen mixed berries, banana, chia seeds, hemp seeds, vegan protein powder, and almond milk in a blender.

2. Blend until smooth and creamy. Add more almond milk or water if needed to reach your desired consistency.

3. Optionally, add ice cubes to make the smoothie colder and more refreshing.

4. Pour into a glass and enjoy immediately as a nutritious breakfast or snack.

Nutritional Information: Calories: 250 kcal Carbohydrates: 25g Protein: 20g Fat:

Vegan Sausage Sandwich Lowdown
Prep time: 10 mins **cooking time**: 10 mins **Servings**: 2

Ingredients:

- 2 vegan sausage patties
- 2 whole grain English muffins, toasted
- 1 ripe avocado, mashed
- 1 tomato, sliced
- Handful of baby spinach leaves
- Salt, to taste
- Freshly ground black pepper, to taste

Preparation Method:

1. Cook vegan sausage patties according to package instructions until heated through and slightly browned.

2. Toast whole-grain English muffins until golden brown.

3. Spread mashed avocado evenly on the bottom halves of the toasted English muffins.

4. Top each with a cooked vegan sausage patty, sliced tomato, and baby spinach leaves.

5. Season with salt and black pepper to taste.

6. Place the remaining halves of the English muffins on top to form sandwiches.

7. Serve immediately and enjoy your Vegan Sausage Sandwich Lowdown for a satisfying breakfast.

Nutritional Information: Calories: 50 kcal Carbohydrates: 30g Protein: 15g Fat: 20g Fiber10g

Keralan Coconut Scramble
Prep Time: 10 minutes **Cooking time:**15 minutes **Servings:** 2

Ingredients:

- 1 tablespoon coconut oil
- 1 small onion, finely chopped
- 2 cloves garlic, minced
- 1 teaspoon grated ginger
- 1 green chilli, finely chopped (optional)
- 1/2 teaspoon ground turmeric
- 1/2 teaspoon ground cumin
- 1/2 teaspoon ground coriander
- 1 cup shredded coconut
- 1 cup chopped mixed vegetables (such as bell peppers, carrots, peas)
- Salt, to taste
- Freshly ground black pepper, to taste
- Fresh cilantro for garnish

Preparation Methods:

1. Heat coconut oil in a skillet over medium heat.

2. Add onions, garlic, ginger, and green chilli (if using). Sauté until onions are translucent.

3. Add ground turmeric, cumin, and coriander. Stir well.

4. Add shredded coconut and chopped vegetables. Cook until vegetables are tender.

5. Season with salt and black pepper. Garnish with fresh cilantro.

Nutritional Value: Calories: 250 kcal Carbohydrates: 15g Protein: 3g Fat: 21g Fiber: 6g

Dandelion Root Latte

Prep Time: 5 minutes **Cooking time:** 5 minutes **Serving**

Ingredients:

- 1 teaspoon dandelion root powder
- 1 cup unsweetened almond milk (or any unsweetened plant-based milk)
- 1 teaspoon maple syrup or stevia (optional for sweetness)
- Ground cinnamon, for garnish (optional)

Preparation Methods:

1. Heat the almond milk in a small saucepan.

2. Whisk in dandelion root powder until it is well combined.

3. Sweeten with maple syrup or stevia if desired.

4. Pour into a mug and sprinkle with ground cinnamon.

Nutritional Value: Calories: 50 kcal Carbohydrates: 3g Protein:1g Fat: 3g Fiber: 1g

Chocolate Protein Chia Pudding

Prep Time: 5 minutes (This recipe is prepared cold) **Servings:** 1

Ingredients:

- 2 tablespoons chia seeds
- 1 cup unsweetened almond milk (or any unsweetened plant-based milk)
- 1 tablespoon cocoa powder
- 1 tablespoon maple syrup or stevia (optional for sweetness)
- Fresh berries, for garnish

Preparation Method:

1. combine chia seeds, almond milk, cocoa powder, and maple syrup in a bowl.

2. Stir well and let it sit in the refrigerator for at least 2 hours or overnight.

3. Stir again before serving, and top with fresh berries.

Nutritional Value: Calories: 200 kcal Carbohydrates: 20g Protein: 7g Fat: 10g Fiber: 12g

Brunch Omelets with Smoky Garlic Mushrooms
Prep Time: 10 minutes **cooking time:** 10 minutes **Servings:** 1

Ingredients:

- 2 large eggs (or vegan egg substitute)
- 1 cup sliced mushrooms
- 2 cloves garlic, minced
- 1 tablespoon olive oil
- Salt, to taste
- Freshly ground black pepper, to taste
- Smoked paprika, for garnish
- Fresh parsley for garnish

Preparation Method:

1. In a bowl, beat eggs until well-mixed.

2. Heat the olive oil in a skillet over medium heat.

3. Add minced garlic and cook until it is fragrant.

4. Add sliced mushrooms and cook until it's tender.

5. Pour beaten eggs into the skillet and cook until it sets.

6. Season with salt and black pepper. Sprinkle with smoked paprika and garnish with fresh parsley.

Nutritional Value: Calories: 300 kcal Carbohydrates: 7g Protein: 20g Fat: 22g Fiber: 3g

Home-made Hash Browns
Prep Time: 15 minutes **cooking time:** 20 minutes **Servings:** 4

Ingredients:

- 4 medium potatoes, peeled and grated
- 1 small onion, finely chopped
- 2 tablespoons olive oil
- Salt, to taste
- Black pepper, to taste
- Paprika, to taste (optional)

- Chopped fresh parsley for garnish (optional)

Preparation Methods:

1. Place grated potatoes in a clean kitchen towel and squeeze out excess moisture.

2. Mix grated potatoes and chopped onion in a large bowl.

3. Season with salt, black pepper, and paprika (if using), and mix well.

4. Heat the olive oil in a skillet over medium heat.

5. Scoop a portion of the potato mixture and shape it into patties.

6. Cook hash brown patties in the skillet for 5-7 minutes on each side until golden brown and crispy.

7. Remove from the skillet and drain on paper towels.

8. Garnish with chopped fresh parsley before serving, if desired.

Nutritional Value: Calories:150 kcal Carbohydrates: 20g Protein: 2g Fat:7g Fiber: 2g

Nutty Vegan Mushroom Sausages
Prep Time:15 minutes **Cooking time**: 20 minutes **Servings:** 6 sausages

Ingredients:

- 8 oz mushrooms, finely chopped
- 1 cup cooked quinoa
- 1/2 cup walnuts, finely chopped
- 2 tablespoons ground flaxseeds
- 1 tablespoon soy sauce or tamari
- 1 teaspoon smoked paprika
- 1/2 teaspoon garlic powder
- Salt, to taste
- Black pepper, to taste
- Olive oil for cooking

Preparation Methods:

1. In a large bowl, combine chopped mushrooms, cooked quinoa, chopped walnuts, ground flaxseeds, soy sauce or tamari, smoked paprika, garlic powder, salt, and black pepper. Mix well to combine.

2. Shape the mixture into sausage patties.

3. Heat olive oil in a skillet over medium heat.

4. Cook sausages for 5-7 minutes on each side or until browned and cooked through.

5. Serve hot with your favourite breakfast sides.

Nutritional Value: Calories: 150 kcal Carbohydrates: 8g Protein: 5g Fat:10g Fiber: 3g

Porridge with Flax seeds, Berries and Banana

Prep Time: 5 minutes **Cooking time:** 10 minutes **Servings:** 2

Ingredients:

- 1 cup rolled oats
- 2 cups water or plant-based milk
- 2 tablespoons ground flaxseeds
- 1/2 cup of mixed berries (such as strawberries, blueberries, raspberries)
- 1 ripe banana, sliced
- Maple syrup or stevia, to taste (optional)
- Chopped nuts or seeds for garnish (optional)

Preparation Methods:

1. bring water or plant-based milk to a boil in a saucepan.

2. Stir in rolled oats and reduce heat to low. Simmer for 5-7 minutes, stirring occasionally, until the oats are cooked and the porridge is creamy.

3. Remove from heat and stir in ground flaxseeds.

4. Divide porridge into bowls and top with mixed berries and sliced banana.

5. Sweeten with maple syrup or stevia if desired.

6. Garnish with chopped nuts or seeds before serving, if desired.

Nutritional Value: Calories: 250 kcal Carbohydrates: 40g Protein: 8g Fat: 6g Fiber: 7g

Super Stuffed Tempeh Sandwich

Prep Time: 15 minutes **Cooking time:** 15 minutes **Servings:** 2

Ingredients:

- 1 package (8 oz) tempeh, sliced into thin strips
- 4 slices whole grain bread
- 2 tablespoons olive oil
- 1 small onion, sliced
- 1 bell pepper, sliced
- 1/2 cup spinach leaves
- Salt, to taste
- Black pepper, to taste
- Hummus for spreading (optional)
- Mustard for spreading (optional)
- Avocado slices, for garnish (optional)
- Tomato slices, for garnish (optional)

Preparation Methods:

1. Heat the olive oil in a skillet over medium heat.

2. Add tempeh slices and cook on each side for 3-4 minutes or until golden brown.

3. Remove tempeh from the skillet and set aside.

4. In the same skillet, add sliced onion and bell pepper. Sauté until softened.

5. Season with salt and black pepper.

6. Toast whole grain bread slices until golden brown.

7. Spread hummus and mustard on the bread slices.

8. Layer tempeh slices, sautéed onion, bell pepper, and spinach leaves on the bread slices.

9. Top with avocado and tomato slices, if desired.

10. Cover with another slice of bread to form sandwiches.

11. Cut sandwiches in half and serve.

Nutritional Value: Calories: 400 kcal Carbohydrates: 40g Protein: 20g Fat: 20g Fiber: 10g

Scrambled Tofu with Fresh Tomatoes & Basil
Prep Time: 10 minutes **Cooking time**:10 minutes **Servings:** 2

Ingredients:

- 1 block (14 oz) firm tofu, drained and crumbled
- 1 tablespoon olive oil
- 1 small onion, finely chopped
- 2 cloves garlic, minced
- 2 medium tomatoes, diced
- Handful of fresh basil leaves, chopped
- Salt, to taste
- Black pepper, to taste
- Turmeric, for colour (optional)
- Nutritional yeast for garnish (optional)

Preparation Method:

1. Heat olive oil in a skillet over medium heat.

2. Add chopped onion and minced garlic. Sauté until softened.

3. Add crumbled tofu to the skillet. Cook for about 5-7 minutes, stirring occasionally.

4. Add diced tomatoes and chopped basil to the skillet. Cook for another 2-3 minutes.

5. Season with salt, black pepper, and turmeric (if using) to taste.

6. Sprinkle with nutritional yeast before serving, if desired.

Nutritional Value: Calories: 200 kcal Carbohydrates: 10g Protein: 15g Fat: 10g Fiber: 4g

Spanish White Wine Lentils

Prep Time: 10 minutes **Cooking time:** 30 minutes **Servings:** 4

Ingredients:

- 1 cup of green or brown lentils, rinsed and drained
- 2 tablespoons olive oil
- 1 onion, finely chopped
- 2 cloves garlic, minced
- 1 carrot, diced
- 1 celery stalk, diced
- 1 teaspoon smoked paprika
- 1/2 teaspoon cumin
- 1/2 teaspoon dried thyme
- 1 bay leaf
- 1/2 cup dry white wine
- 2 cups vegetable broth
- Salt, to taste
- Black pepper, to taste
- Fresh parsley, chopped, for garnish (optional)

Preparation Methods:

1. Heat the olive oil in a large pot over medium heat. Add onion and garlic, and sauté until softened.

2. Add carrot and celery and cook until slightly softened.

3. Stir in smoked paprika, cumin, thyme, and bay leaf, and cook for another minute.

4. Add lentils and white wine and stir until the wine evaporates.

5. Pour in the vegetable broth, boil, then reduce the heat and simmer for 20-25 minutes or until lentils are tender.

6. Season it with black pepper and salt to taste.

7. Garnish it with fresh parsley before serving, if desired.

Nutritional Value: Calories: 250 kcal Carbohydrates: 30g Protein: 12g Fat: 8g Fiber: 10g

One Pot Rainbow Pasta

Prep Time: 10 minutes **Cooking time**: 20 minutes **Servings:** 4

Ingredients:

- 8 oz whole grain pasta (of your choice)
- 1 tablespoon olive oil
- 1 onion, diced
- 2 cloves garlic, minced
- 1 bell pepper, diced
- 1 zucchini, diced
- 1 cup cherry tomatoes, halved
- 2 cups vegetable broth
- 1/2 teaspoon dried basil
- 1/2 teaspoon dried oregano
- Salt, to taste
- Black pepper, to taste
- Fresh basil, chopped, for garnish (optional)

Preparation Methods:

1. heat the olive oil over medium heat in a large pot. Add onion and garlic, and sauté until softened.

2. Add bell pepper, zucchini, and cherry tomatoes; cook for 5-7 minutes or until vegetables are tender.

3. Stir in dried basil and oregano.

4. Add vegetable broth and pasta to the pot. Bring to a boil, then reduce heat and simmer for 10-12 minutes or until pasta is cooked and most liquid is absorbed.

5. Season with black pepper and salt to taste.

6. Garnish with fresh basil before serving, if desired.

Nutritional Value: Calories: 300 kcal
Carbohydrates: 50g Protein: 10g Fat: 7g
Fiber: 8g

Sweet Potato, Spicy Black Beans & Guacamole
Prep Time: 15 minutes **Cooking time:** 30 minutes **Serving: 4**

Ingredients:

- 2 large sweet potatoes, peeled and chopped
- 1 tablespoon olive oil
- 1 onion, diced
- 2 cloves garlic, minced
- 1 teaspoon ground cumin
- 1 teaspoon chilli powder
- 1 can of (15 oz) black beans, drained and rinsed
- Salt, to taste
- Black pepper, to taste
- Guacamole, for serving
- Fresh cilantro, chopped, for garnish (optional)

Preparation Methods:

1. Preheat the oven to 400°F (200°C).

2. Toss diced sweet potatoes with olive oil, salt, and pepper. Spread them on a baking sheet and roast for 20-25 minutes or until tender and lightly browned.

3. In a large skillet, heat olive oil over medium heat. Add onion and garlic, and sauté until softened.

4. Stir in ground cumin and chilli powder, and cook for another minute.

5. Add black beans to the skillet and cook until heated through.

6. Season with salt and black pepper to taste.

7. Serve roasted sweet potatoes and spicy black beans with guacamole on the side.

8. Garnish with fresh cilantro before serving, if desired.

Nutritional Value: Calories: 300 kcal
Carbohydrates: 45g Protein: 10g Fat: 10g
Fiber: 12g

Aubergine & Green Lentil Koftas
Prep Time: 20 minutes **cooking time:** 30 minutes **Servings:** 12 koftas

Ingredients:

- 1 cup cooked green lentils

- 1 large eggplant (aubergine), diced
- 1 onion, finely chopped
- 2 cloves garlic, minced

- 2 tablespoons olive oil
- 1 teaspoon ground cumin
- 1 teaspoon ground coriander
- 1/2 teaspoon smoked paprika
- Salt, to taste
- Black pepper, to taste
- Fresh parsley, chopped, for garnish (optional)

Preparation Methods:

1. Preheat the oven to 400°F (200°C).

2. Place diced eggplant on a baking sheet and drizzle with olive oil, salt, and pepper. Roast for 20-25 minutes or until tender and golden brown.

3. In a large skillet, heat olive oil over medium heat. Add onion and garlic, and sauté until softened.

4. Add cooked green lentils and roasted eggplant to the skillet. Mash the mixture with a fork or potato masher.

5. Stir in ground cumin, coriander, smoked paprika, salt, and black pepper.

6. Shape the mixture into small kofta balls.

7. Heat olive oil in a skillet over medium heat. Cook koftas for 3-4 minutes on each side or until golden brown.

8. Garnish with fresh parsley before serving, if desired.

Nutritional Value: Calories: 100 kcal Carbohydrates: 15g Protein: 5g Fat: 3g Fiber:5g

Tortilla De Patatas
Prep Time:15 minutes **Cooking time**: 30 minutes **Servings:** 4

Ingredients:

- 4 medium potatoes, thinly sliced
- 1 onion, thinly sliced
- 6 large eggs
- 2 tablespoons olive oil
- Salt, to taste
- Black pepper, to taste
- Fresh parsley, chopped, for garnish (optional)

Preparation Methods:

1. whisk together eggs, salt, and black pepper in a large bowl.

2. Heat the olive oil in a large skillet over medium heat. Add thinly sliced potatoes and onion, and cook until potatoes are tender and lightly golden brown.

3. Transfer cooked potatoes and onion to the bowl with beaten eggs. Mix well to combine.

4. Heat a little more olive oil in the same skillet. Pour the egg and potato mixture into the skillet.

5. Cook for 5-7 minutes or until the bottom is set and lightly browned.

6. Carefully flip the tortilla using a large plate. Slide it back into the skillet and cook for another 5-7 minutes or until cooked.

7. Garnish it with fresh parsley before serving, if desired.

Nutritional Value: Calories: 250 kcal Carbohydrates: 20g Protein:10g Fat:15g Fiber: 3g

Broccoli, Lemon & Mint Risotto
Prep Time:10 minutes **cooking time**:30 minutes **Servings**:4

Ingredients:

- 1 cup Arborio rice
- 4 cups vegetable broth
- 1 tablespoon olive oil
- 1 onion, finely chopped
- 2 cloves garlic, minced
- 2 cups broccoli florets
- Zest of 1 lemon
- 2 tablespoons fresh lemon juice
- 2 tablespoons fresh mint, chopped
- Salt, to taste
- Black pepper, to taste
- Vegan parmesan cheese for garnish (optional)

Preparation Methods:

1. In a saucepan, heat vegetable broth and keep it warm over low heat.

2. heat the olive oil over medium heat in a large skillet. Add chopped onion and minced garlic, and sauté until it's softened.

3. Add Arborio rice to the skillet and cook for 1-2 minutes, stirring constantly.

4. Ladle in a scoop of warm vegetable broth to the skillet, stirring continuously until absorbed.

5. Continue adding broth, one ladleful at a time, stirring frequently, until the rice is creamy and tender (about 20-25 minutes).

6. Stir in broccoli florets during the last 5 minutes of cooking.

7. Once the rice and broccoli are cooked, stir in lemon zest, lemon juice, and chopped mint.

8. Season it with black pepper and salt to taste.

9. Serve hot, garnished with vegan parmesan cheese if desired.

Nutritional Value: Calories: 300 kcal Carbohydrates: 50g Protein: 8g Fat: 7g Fiber: 5g

Quick & Easy Chana Masala

Prep Time: 10 minutes **Cooking time:** 20 minutes **Servings:** 4

Ingredients:

- 2 cans (15 oz each) chickpeas, drained and rinsed
- 1 tablespoon olive oil
- 1 onion, finely chopped
- 2 cloves garlic, minced
- 1-inch piece ginger, grated
- 1 green chilli, finely chopped (optional)
- 2 teaspoons ground cumin
- 2 teaspoons ground coriander
- 1 teaspoon turmeric powder
- 1 teaspoon garam masala
- 1 can (14 oz) diced tomatoes
- Salt, to taste
- Fresh cilantro, chopped, for garnish (optional)

Preparation Methods:

1. Heat the olive oil in a large skillet over medium heat. Add chopped onion and sauté until it is soft.

2. Add minced garlic, grated ginger, and chopped green chilli (if using), cook for another minute.

3. Stir in ground cumin, coriander, turmeric powder, and garam masala until fragrant.

4. Add diced tomatoes to the skillet and cook for a few minutes until slightly thickened.

5. Add drained and rinsed chickpeas to the skillet and stir to combine.

6. Simmer for 10-15 minutes, stirring occasionally, until the flavours meld together and the sauce thickens.

7. Season with salt to taste.

8. Garnish with chopped fresh cilantro before serving, if desired.

Nutritional Value: Calories: 250 kcal Carbohydrates: 40g Protein: 10g Fat: 6g Fiber: 10g

Raw Lasagne

Prep Time: 30 minutes (plus soaking time for cashews, if using) **Cooking time**: 0 minutes **Servings:** 4

Ingredients:

- 1 large zucchini, thinly sliced lengthwise
- 1 large carrot, thinly sliced lengthwise
- 1 cup cherry tomatoes, halved
- 1 cup spinach leaves
- 1 cup raw cashews, soaked for at least 4 hours (optional, for cashew cheese)
- 2 tablespoons nutritional yeast
- 2 tablespoons lemon juice
- 1 clove garlic, minced
- Salt, to taste
- Black pepper, to taste
- Fresh basil leaves for garnish

Preparation Methods:

1. drain soaked cashews and place them in a blender if using cashew cheese. Add the nutritional yeast, lemon juice, garlic, salt, and pepper. Blend until smooth and creamy, adding water to reach desired consistency.

2. Layer zucchini slices on the bottom of a serving dish to form the first layer of "pasta".

3. Spread a layer of cashew cheese (if using) over the zucchini slices.

4. Top with a layer of carrot slices, cherry tomatoes, and spinach leaves.

5. Repeat the layers until all ingredients are used up, finishing with a layer of vegetables on top.

6. Garnish with fresh basil leaves.

7. Refrigerate for at least 30 minutes before serving to allow the flavours to meld.

Nutritional Value: Calories: 200 kcal (without cashew cheese) Carbohydrates: 20g Protein: 8g Fat: 12g Fiber: 6g

Easy Quiche with Broccoli & Sundried Tomatoes

Prep Time: 15 minutes **Cooking time**: 40 minutes **Servings:** 6

Ingredients:

- 1 ready-made vegan pie crust
- 1 cup broccoli florets, steamed and chopped
- 1/2 cup sundried tomatoes, chopped
- 1/2 cup diced onion
- 1 tablespoon olive oil

- 1 cup of unsweetened almond milk (or any plant-based milk)
- 1/4 cup chickpea flour
- 2 tablespoons nutritional yeast
- 1 teaspoon dried thyme
- Salt, to taste
- Black pepper, to taste

Preparation Methods:

1. Preheat the oven to 375°F (190°C).

2. In a skillet, heat the olive oil over medium heat. Add diced onion and cook until it's softened.

3. Whisk almond milk, chickpea flour, nutritional yeast, dried thyme, salt, and black pepper in a mixing bowl.

4. Place steamed broccoli florets and chopped sundried tomatoes in the bottom of the pie crust. Top with cooked onion.

5. Pour the almond milk mixture over the vegetables in the pie crust.

6. Bake in the preheated oven for about 35-40 minutes or until the quiche is set and golden brown on the top.

7. Allow to cool for a few minutes before slicing and serving.

Nutritional Value: Calories: 250 kcal Carbohydrates:25g Protein: 7g Fat: 15g Fiber: 5g

Chickpea, Sweet Potato & Tomato Curry
Prep Time:15 minutes Cooking time: 30 minutes Servings: 4

Ingredients:

- 1 tablespoon olive oil
- 1 onion, diced
- 2 cloves garlic, minced
- 1-inch piece ginger, grated
- 2 teaspoons curry powder
- 1 teaspoon ground cumin
- 1 teaspoon ground coriander
- 1/2 teaspoon turmeric powder
- 1/4 teaspoon cayenne pepper (optional for heat)
- 2 cups diced sweet potatoes
- 1 can (15 oz) chickpeas, drained and rinsed
- 1 can (14 oz) diced tomatoes
- 1 cup vegetable broth
- Salt, to taste
- Black pepper, to taste
- Fresh cilantro, chopped, for garnish

Preparation Methods:

1. Heat the olive oil in a large skillet over medium heat. Add diced onion and cook until it's softened.

2. Add minced garlic and grated ginger to the skillet and cook for another minute.

3. Stir in curry powder, ground cumin, ground coriander, turmeric powder, and cayenne pepper (if using), and cook until fragrant.

4. Add diced sweet potatoes, chickpeas, tomatoes, and vegetable broth to the skillet. Stir to combine.

5. Bring to a boil, then reduce heat and simmer for 20-25 minutes or until sweet potatoes are tender and the curry has thickened.

6. Season with salt and black pepper to taste.

7. Garnish with fresh cilantro before serving.

Nutritional Value: Calories: 300 kcal Carbohydrates: 45g Protein: 10g Fat: 8g Fiber: 12g

Chana Balti
Prep Time: 15 minutes **Cooking time**: 30 minutes **Servings:** 4

Ingredients:

- 2 tablespoons vegetable oil
- 1 onion, finely chopped
- 2 cloves garlic, minced
- 1-inch piece ginger, grated
- 1 green chilli, finely chopped (optional)
- 1 tablespoon Balti curry paste
- 1 teaspoon ground cumin
- 1 teaspoon ground coriander
- 1 teaspoon garam masala
- 1 can (15 oz) chickpeas, drained and rinsed
- 1 can (14 oz) diced tomatoes
- 1/2 cup vegetable broth
- Salt, to taste
- Black pepper, to taste
- Fresh cilantro, chopped, for garnish

Preparation Methods:

1. Heat the vegetable oil in a large skillet over medium heat. Add finely chopped onion and cook until it is soft.

2. Add minced garlic, grated ginger, and chopped green chilli (if using), cook for another minute.

3. Stir in Balti curry paste, ground cumin, coriander, and garam masala until fragrant.

4. Add drained chickpeas, diced tomatoes, and vegetable broth to the skillet. Stir to combine.

5. Bring to a boil, then reduce heat and simmer for 20-25 minutes or until the curry has thickened.

6. Season with salt and black pepper to taste.

7. Garnish with fresh cilantro before serving.

Nutritional Value: Calories: 250 kcal Carbohydrates: 30g Protein: 8g Fat:10g Fiber: 8g

Sumac & Ginger-Garlic Pan-fried Tofu

Prep Time: 10 minutes **Cooking time:**15 minutes **Servings: 4**

Ingredients:

- 1 block (14 oz) firm tofu, drained and sliced into cubes
- 2 tablespoons olive oil
- 2 cloves garlic, minced
- 1-inch piece ginger, grated
- 1 teaspoon sumac
- 1 teaspoon paprika
- Salt, to taste
- Black pepper, to taste
- Fresh parsley, chopped, for garnish

Preparation Methods:

1. Heat olive oil in a large skillet over medium heat. Add minced garlic and grated ginger, and cook until it's fragrant.

2. Add tofu cubes to the skillet. Pan-fry it until it's golden brown on all sides.

3. Sprinkle sumac, paprika, salt, and black pepper over the tofu. Stir to coat evenly.

4. Continue to cook for another 5-7 minutes or until tofu is crispy and golden.

5. Garnish with fresh parsley before serving.

Nutritional Value: Calories:150 kcal Carbohydrates: 4g Protein: 8g Fat: 12g Fiber: 2g

Multi-Grain Risotto

Prep Time: 10 minutes **Cooking time:** 40 minutes **Servings: 4**

Ingredients:

- 1 cup Arborio rice
- 1/2 cup quinoa, rinsed
- 4 cups vegetable broth
- 1 tablespoon olive oil
- 1 onion, finely chopped
- 2 cloves garlic, minced
- 1 cup of mixed vegetables (such as peas, carrots, bell peppers)
- 1/4 cup nutritional yeast
- Salt, to taste

- Black pepper, to taste
- Fresh parsley, chopped, for garnish

Preparation Methods:

1. bring vegetable broth to a simmer in a saucepan and keep warm over low heat.

2. In a big skillet, heat olive oil over medium heat. Add finely chopped onion and minced garlic, and cook until softened.

3. Add Arborio rice and rinsed quinoa to the skillet. Cook for 1-2 minutes, stirring constantly.

4. Stir frequently; add vegetable broth to the skillet, one ladleful at a time. Allow the liquid to absorb before adding more.

5. Continue cooking and adding broth until the rice and quinoa are tender and creamy (about 30-35 minutes).

6. Stir in mixed vegetables during the last 10 minutes of cooking.

7. Once cooked, stir in nutritional yeast and season with salt and black pepper to taste.

8. Garnish with fresh parsley before serving.

Nutritional Value: Calories: 300 kcal Carbohydrates: 50g Protein: 8g Fat: 7g Fiber: 6g.

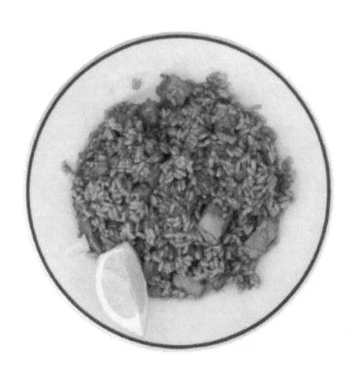

Spicy Vegan Bean Burgers

Prep Time: 15 minutes **cooking time**: 20 minutes **Servings:** 4 burgers

Ingredients:

- 1 can (15 oz) mixed beans, drained and rinsed
- 1/2 cup breadcrumbs
- 1/4 cup finely chopped onion
- 2 cloves garlic, minced
- 1 teaspoon ground cumin
- 1 teaspoon paprika
- 1/2 teaspoon chilli powder
- Salt, to taste
- Black pepper, to taste
- Olive oil for cooking
- Burger buns and toppings of your choice

Preparation Methods:

1. mash the mixed beans with a fork or potato masher until smooth in a large mixing basin.

2. Add breadcrumbs, chopped onion, minced garlic, ground cumin, paprika, chilli powder, salt, and black pepper to the bowl. Mix until well combined.

3. Divide the mixture into 4 equal portions, then form each portion into a patty.

4. Heat the olive oil in a skillet over medium heat. Cook the patties on each side

for 4-5 minutes until golden brown and heated through.

5. Serve the bean burgers on burger buns with your favourite toppings.

Nutritional Value: Calories: 200 kcal (without bun and toppings) Carbohydrates: 30g Protein:10g Fat: 5g Fiber: 8g

Middle-Eastern Nutty Millet Pilaf
Prep Time: 10 minutes **Cooking time**: 25 minutes **Servings:** 4

Ingredients:

- 1 cup millet, rinsed
- 2 cups vegetable broth
- 1/4 cup chopped almonds
- 1/4 cup chopped pistachios
- 1/4 cup chopped dried apricots
- 1/4 cup chopped dried figs
- 1 tablespoon olive oil
- 1 onion, finely chopped
- 2 cloves garlic, minced
- 1 teaspoon ground cumin
- 1 teaspoon ground coriander
- Salt, to taste
- Black pepper, to taste
- Fresh parsley, chopped, for garnish

Preparation Methods:

1. In a saucepan, heat the olive oil over medium heat. Add finely chopped onion and minced garlic, and cook until softened.

2. Add rinsed millet to the saucepan. Toast for 2-3 minutes, stirring constantly.

3. Pour vegetable broth into the saucepan. Bring to a boil, then reduce heat and simmer for 15-20 minutes or until millet is cooked and liquid is absorbed.

4. In a separate skillet, toast chopped almonds and pistachios over medium heat until lightly golden and fragrant.

5. Once the millet is cooked, fluff it with a fork and stir in chopped dried apricots, figs, toasted almonds, pistachios, ground cumin, coriander, salt, and black pepper.

6. Garnish with fresh parsley before serving.

Nutritional Value: Calories: 300 kcal Carbohydrates: 40g Protein: 8g Fat: 12g Fiber: 6g

Warm Beetroot & Quinoa Tabbouleh

Prep Time: 15 minutes **Cooking time**: 20 minutes **Servings:** 4

Ingredients:

- 1 cup quinoa, rinsed
- 2 cups water
- 2 large beetroots, cooked and diced
- 1 cucumber, diced
- 1 cup cherry tomatoes, halved
- 1/4 cup chopped fresh parsley
- 1/4 cup chopped fresh mint
- 2 tablespoons olive oil
- 2 tablespoons lemon juice
- Salt, to taste
- Black pepper, to taste

Preparation Methods:

1. In a saucepan, bring water to a boil. Add rinsed quinoa and reduce heat to low. Cover and simmer for 15-20 minutes or until quinoa is cooked and water is absorbed.

2. In a large mixing bowl, combine cooked quinoa, diced beetroots, cucumber, halved cherry tomatoes, chopped fresh parsley, and chopped fresh mint.

3. whisk together olive oil, lemon juice, salt, and black pepper in a small bowl to make the dressing.

4. Pour the dressing over the quinoa salad and mix thoroughly.

5. Serve warm or at room temperature.

Nutritional Value: Calories: 250 kcal Carbohydrates:35g Protein: 7g Fat: 10g Fiber: 6g

Pasta with Aubergine & Artichokes

Prep Time:10 minutes **Cooking time**: 20 minutes **Servings:** 4

Ingredients:

- 8 oz pasta of your choice
- 1 large aubergine (eggplant), diced
- 1 can (14 oz) artichoke hearts, drained and quartered
- 2 cloves garlic, minced
- 2 tablespoons olive oil
- 1 teaspoon dried oregano
- 1/2 teaspoon chilli flakes
- Salt, to taste
- Black pepper, to taste
- Fresh basil, chopped, for garnish (optional)

Preparation Methods:

1. Cook pasta according to package instructions. Drain and set aside.

2. heat the olive oil over medium heat in a large skillet. Add minced garlic and cook until it's fragrant.

3. Add diced aubergine to the skillet. Cook until softened and lightly browned.

4. Stir in quartered artichoke hearts, dried oregano, chilli flakes, salt, and black pepper. Cook for another 5 minutes.

5. Add the cooked pasta to the skillet and toss until well combined.

6. Garnish it with fresh chopped basil before serving, if desired

Nutritional Value: Calories 300 kcal Carbohydrates: 45g Protein: 8g Fat: 10g Fiber: 6g

Easy Home-made Tofu Burgers

Prep Time: 15 minutes **cooking time**: 20 minutes **Servings:** 4 burgers

Ingredients:

- 1 block (14 oz) firm tofu, drained and pressed
- 1/4 cup breadcrumbs
- 1/4 cup finely chopped onion
- 2 cloves garlic, minced
- 1 tablespoon soy sauce
- 1 tablespoon nutritional yeast
- 1 teaspoon smoked paprika
- Salt, to taste
- Black pepper, to taste
- Olive oil for cooking
- Burger buns and toppings of your choice

Preparation Methods:

1. In a large mixing bowl, crumble the pressed tofu using your hands.

2. Add breadcrumbs, chopped onion, minced garlic, soy sauce, nutritional yeast, smoked paprika, salt, and black pepper to the bowl. Mix until well combined.

3. Divide the mixture into 4 equal parts and shape each into a patty.

4. Heat the olive oil in a skillet over medium heat. Cook the tofu patties on each side for 4-5 minutes until golden brown and heated through.

5. Serve the tofu burgers on burger buns with your favourite toppings.

Nutritional Value: Calories: 200 kcal (without bun and toppings) Carbohydrates: 15g Protein: 12g Fat: 8g Fiber: 3g

Sausages with Apple Mustard Mash & Gravy
Prep time: 15 minutes **Cooking time:** 30 minutes **Servings:** 4

Ingredients:

- 4 vegan sausages
- 4 large potatoes, peeled and chopped
- 2 apples, peeled, cored and chopped
- 2 tablespoons whole-grain mustard
- ¼ cup of unsweetened almond milk (or any plant-based milk)
- Salt, to taste
- Black pepper, to taste
- 1 tablespoon olive oil
- 1 onion, finely chopped
- 2 cloves garlic, minced
- 2 tablespoons all-purpose flour
- 2 cups vegetable broth
- Fresh parsley, chopped, for garnish

Preparation Methods:

1. Cook vegan sausages according to package instructions.

2. In a large pot, boil chopped potatoes until tender. Drain and return to the pot.

3. Add chopped apples, whole grain mustard, almond milk, salt, and black pepper to the pot with the cooked potatoes. Mash until smooth and creamy.

4. Heat the olive oil in a skillet over medium heat. Add finely chopped onion and minced garlic, and cook until softened.

5. Add the all-purpose flour to the cooked onion and garlic. Stir to combine.

6. Pour the vegetable broth into the skillet gradually, stirring constantly to prevent lumps from forming.

7. Cook until the gravy thickens, then season with salt and black pepper to taste.

8. Serve vegan sausages with apple mustard mash and gravy. Garnish with fresh chopped parsley.

Nutritional Value: Calories: 350 kcal Carbohydrates: 45g Protein: 10g Fat 15 Fiber: 8g

Thai Sweet Potato Cakes
Prep Time: 15 minutes **Cooking time:** 20 minutes **Servings:** 8 cakes

Ingredients:

- 2 large sweet potatoes, peeled and grated
- 1/2 cup chickpea flour

- 2 tablespoons Thai red curry paste
- 1 tablespoon soy sauce
- 1 tablespoon lime juice
- 1 tablespoon chopped fresh cilantro
- 1 tablespoon chopped fresh mint

- Salt, to taste
- Black pepper, to taste
- Olive oil for cooking

Preparation Methods:

1. combine grated sweet potatoes, chickpea flour, Thai red curry paste, soy sauce, lime juice, chopped cilantro, chopped mint, salt, and black pepper in a large mixing bowl. Mix until well combined.

2. Divide the mixture into 8 equal portions and form each into a patty.

3. Heat the olive oil in a skillet over medium heat. Cook the sweet potato cakes for 4-5 minutes on each side or until golden brown and cooked through.

4. Serve hot with your favourite dipping sauce or salad.

Nutritional Value: Calories: 150 kcal Carbohydrates: 25g Protein: 5g Fat: 3g Fiber: 4g

Baked Rice Pilaf with Squash

Prep Time: 15 minutes **Cooking time**: 45 minutes **Servings:** 6

Ingredients:

- 1 cup long-grain white rice
- 2 cups vegetable broth
- 2 cups diced butternut squash
- 1 onion, finely chopped
- 2 cloves garlic, minced
- 1 teaspoon dried thyme
- 1/2 teaspoon ground cumin
- Salt, to taste
- Black pepper, to taste
- Olive oil for cooking

Preparation Methods:

1. Preheat the oven to 375°F (190°C).

2. Heat the olive oil in a large skillet over medium heat. Add finely chopped onion and minced garlic, and cook until softened.

3. Add diced butternut squash to the skillet. Cook for 5-7 minutes or until slightly tender.

4. Stir in long-grain white rice, dried thyme, ground cumin, salt, and black pepper. Cook for another 2-3 minutes.

5. Transfer the rice and squash mixture to a baking dish. Pour vegetable broth over the mixture.

6. Cover the baking dish with foil and bake in the oven for 30-35 minutes or until the rice is cooked and the liquid is absorbed.

7. Fluff the rice pilaf with a fork before serving.

Nutritional Value: Calories: 200 kcal Carbohydrates: 40g Protein: 4g Fat: 2gFiber: 3g

Easy Vegan Spaghetti Bolognese
Prep Time: 15 minutes **Cooking time**: 30 minutes **Servings:** 4

Ingredients:

- 8 oz spaghetti
- 1 tablespoon olive oil
- 1 onion, finely chopped
- 2 cloves garlic, minced
- 1 carrot, grated
- 1 celery stalk, finely chopped
- 1 bell pepper, diced
- 1 cup cooked lentils
- 1 can (14 oz) diced tomatoes
- 2 tablespoons tomato paste
- 1 teaspoon dried oregano
- 1 teaspoon dried basil
- Salt, to taste
- Black pepper, to taste

Preparation Methods:

1. Cook spaghetti according to package instructions. Drain and set aside.

2. heat the olive oil over medium heat in a big skillet. Add finely chopped onion and minced garlic, and cook until softened.

3. Add grated carrot, finely chopped celery, and diced bell pepper to the skillet. Cook the vegetables for 5-7 minutes or until they are soft.

4. Stir in cooked lentils, diced tomatoes, tomato paste, dried oregano, dried basil, salt, and black pepper. Simmer for 10-15 minutes, stirring occasionally.

5. Serve vegan Bolognese sauce over cooked spaghetti.

Nutritional Value: Calories: 300 kcal (without spaghetti) Carbohydrates: 40g Protein: 10g Fat: 8g Fiber:10g

Simple Speedy Dhal
Prep Time: 10 minutes **Cooking time**: 25 minutes **Servings:** 4

Ingredients:

- 1 cup red lentils
- 3 cups water

- 1 tablespoon olive oil
- 1 onion, finely chopped
- 2 cloves garlic, minced
- 1 teaspoon ground cumin

49

- 1 teaspoon ground turmeric
- 1 teaspoon ground coriander
- Salt, to taste
- Black pepper, to taste
- Fresh cilantro, chopped, for garnish

Preparation Methods:

1. Rinse red lentils under cold water until the water runs clear.

2. In a saucepan, combine red lentils and water. Bring to a boil, then reduce heat and simmer for 15-20 minutes or until lentils are soft and cooked.

3. heat the olive oil over medium heat in a separate skillet. Add finely chopped onion and minced garlic, and cook until softened.

4. Stir in ground cumin, ground turmeric, and ground coriander. Cook for another minute.

5. Add the cooked lentils to the skillet with the spices. Season with salt and black pepper to taste.

6. Cook for 5-7 minutes, stirring occasionally, until the flavours are well combined.

7. Garnish with chopped fresh cilantro before serving.

Nutritional Value: Calories: 200 kcal Carbohydrates: 30g Protein: 10g Fat: 5g Fiber:10g

Chilli non-Carne

Prep Time: 15 minutes **Cooking time**: 30 minutes **Servings:** 6

Ingredients:

- 1 tablespoon olive oil
- 1 onion, finely chopped
- 2 cloves garlic, minced
- 1 bell pepper, diced
- 1 carrot, grated
- 1 celery stalk, finely chopped
- 1 can of (14 oz) kidney beans, drained and rinsed
- 1 can of (14 oz) black beans, drained and rinsed
- 1 can of (14 oz) diced tomatoes
- 2 tablespoons tomato paste
- 1 tablespoon chilli powder
- 1 teaspoon ground cumin
- 1 teaspoon smoked paprika
- Salt, to taste
- Black pepper, to taste
- Fresh cilantro, chopped, for garnish (optional)

Preparation Methods:

1. heat the olive oil over medium heat in a big skillet. Add finely chopped onion and minced garlic, and cook until softened.

2. Add diced bell pepper, grated carrot, and finely chopped celery to the skillet. Cook the vegetables for 5-7 minutes or until they are tender.

3. Stir in drained and rinsed kidney beans, drained and rinsed black beans, diced tomatoes, tomato paste, chilli powder, ground cumin, smoked paprika, salt, and black pepper.

4. Simmer for 15-20 minutes, stirring occasionally, until the flavours are combined and the chilli thickens.

5. Serve hot, garnished with chopped fresh cilantro if desired.

Nutritional Value: Calories: 250 kcal Carbohydrates: 40g Protein: 10g Fat: 5g Fiber: 12g

Easy Vegan Fried Eggs

Prep Time: 10 minutes **cooking time**:10 minutes **Servings:** 4 "eggs"

Ingredients:

- 1 block (14 oz) firm tofu
- 2 tablespoons nutritional yeast
- 1 tablespoon soy sauce
- 1/2 teaspoon turmeric powder
- Salt, to taste
- Black salt (kala namak), to taste (for egg flavour)
- Olive oil for cooking

Preparation Methods:

1. Drain the firm tofu and slice it into 4 "egg-sized" pieces.

2. Mix nutritional yeast, soy sauce, turmeric powder, salt, and black salt in a shallow dish.

3. Coat each tofu slice with the seasoning mixture, ensuring they are well coated on all sides.

4. Heat the olive oil in a skillet over medium heat. Add the seasoned tofu slices to the skillet.

5. Cook for 3-4 minutes on each side until golden brown and heated through.

6. Serve hot as vegan "fried eggs."

Nutritional Value: Calories: 100 kcal Carbohydrates: 3g Protein:10g Fat: 6g Fiber1g

Layered Festive Roast with Vegan Gravy

Prep Time: 20 minutes **cooking time:** 1 hour 30 minutes **Servings:** 6-8

Ingredients:

- 2 cups cooked lentils
- 1 cup cooked quinoa
- 1 cup of chopped nuts (such as walnuts or pecans)
- 1 cup breadcrumbs
- 1 onion, finely chopped
- 2 cloves garlic, minced
- 2 tablespoons soy sauce
- 1 tablespoon olive oil
- 1 tablespoon ground flaxseeds + 3 tablespoons water (flaxseed "egg")
- 1 teaspoon dried thyme
- 1 teaspoon dried rosemary
- Salt, to taste
- Black pepper, to taste
- Vegan gravy (store-bought or homemade) for serving

Preparation Methods:

1. Preheat the oven to 375°F (190°C).

2. In a large mixing bowl, combine cooked lentils, cooked quinoa, chopped nuts, breadcrumbs, finely chopped onion, minced garlic, soy sauce, olive oil, flaxseed "egg," dried thyme, dried rosemary, salt, and black pepper. Mix until well combined.

3. Transfer half of the mixture into a greased loaf pan, pressing firmly to form the first layer.

4. Spread a layer of vegan gravy over the mixture in the loaf pan.

5. Add the remaining mixture to the gravy layer, pressing down firmly to form the second layer.

6. Cover the loaf pan with foil and bake in the oven for 1 hour.

7. Take off the foil and bake for an additional 15-20 minutes or until the top is crispy and golden brown

8. Allow the roast to cool for a few minutes before slicing. Serve hot with additional vegan gravy.

Nutritional Value: Calories: 300 kcal Carbohydrates: 30g Protein: 12g Fat: 15g Fiber:

Spring Greens Spanakopita Pie

Prep Time: 30 minutes **cooking time:** 45 minutes **Servings:** 8-10

Ingredients:

- 1 package (16 oz) phyllo pastry sheets, thawed
- 2 tablespoons olive oil
- 1 onion, finely chopped
- 4 cloves garlic, minced
- 1 lb. mixed spring greens (such as spinach, kale, chard), chopped
- 1 cup chopped fresh dill
- 1 cup chopped fresh parsley
- 1 cup vegan feta cheese, crumbled
- Salt, to taste
- Black pepper, to taste
- Vegan butter or olive oil for brushing

Preparation Methods:

1. Preheat the oven to 375°F (190°C). Grease a 9x13-inch baking dish.

2. heat the olive oil over medium heat in a large skillet. Add finely chopped onion and minced garlic, and cook until softened.

3. Add chopped spring greens to the skillet. Cook until wilted, then remove from heat.

4. Stir in chopped fresh dill, chopped fresh parsley, crumbled vegan feta cheese, salt, and black pepper. Mix until well combined.

5. Layer half of the phyllo pastry sheets in the greased baking dish, brushing each sheet with melted vegan butter or olive oil.

6. Spread the spring greens mixture evenly over the phyllo pastry layer.

7. Top with the remaining phyllo pastry sheets, brushing each with melted vegan butter or olive oil.

8. Using a sharp knife, Score the top layer of phyllo pastry into squares or triangles.

9. Bake in the oven for 35-45 minutes or until the phyllo pastry is golden brown and crispy.

10. Let the spanakopita pie cool for a few minutes before slicing. Serve warm or at room temperature.

Nutritional Value: Calories: 250 kcal Carbohydrates: 25g Protein: 8g Fat: 15g Fiber: 5g

Vegan Chicken Tikka Masala

Prep Time: 20 minutes **Cooking time**: 40 minutes **Servings:** 4

Ingredients:

- 1 package (14 oz) vegan chicken substitute, diced
- 1 onion, finely chopped
- 2 cloves garlic, minced
- 1 bell pepper, diced
- 1 can (14 oz) diced tomatoes
- 1 can (14 oz) coconut milk
- 2 tablespoons tomato paste
- 2 tablespoons olive oil
- 2 tablespoons garam masala
- 1 teaspoon ground cumin
- 1 teaspoon ground coriander
- 1/2 teaspoon turmeric powder
- Salt, to taste
- Black pepper, to taste
- Fresh cilantro, chopped, for garnish
- Cooked rice or naan for serving

Preparation Methods:

1. heat the olive oil over medium heat in a large skillet. Add finely chopped onion and minced garlic, and cook until softened.

2. Add diced vegan chicken substitute and diced bell pepper to the skillet. Cook until lightly browned.

3. Stir in diced tomatoes, coconut milk, tomato paste, garam masala, ground cumin, coriander, turmeric powder, salt, and black pepper. Simmer for 20-25 minutes, stirring occasionally.

4. Serve hot overcooked rice or with naan, garnished with chopped fresh cilantro.

Nutritional Value: Calories: 350 kcal (excluding rice/naan) Carbohydrates: 15g Protein: 10g Fat 25g Fiber: 5g

Deep South Pasta Casserole

Prep Time: 20 minutes **Cooking time**: 45 minutes **Servings** 6

Ingredients:

- 8 oz pasta of your choice
- 1 can of (14 oz) black-eyed peas, drained and rinsed
- 1 can (14 oz) diced tomatoes
- 1 bell pepper, diced
- 1 onion, finely chopped
- 2 cloves garlic, minced
- 1 cup vegetable broth
- 1 tablespoon olive oil
- 1 teaspoon dried thyme
- 1 teaspoon smoked paprika
- Salt, to taste
- Black pepper, to taste
- Vegan cheese, grated, for topping (optional)
- Fresh parsley, chopped, for garnish

Preparation Methods:

1. Preheat the oven to 375°F (190°C). Grease a baking dish.

2. Cook pasta according to package instructions. Drain and set aside.

3. Heat the olive oil in a big skillet over medium heat. Add finely chopped onion and minced garlic, and cook until softened.

4. Add diced bell pepper to the skillet. Cook for 5 minutes.

5. Stir in drained and rinsed black-eyed peas, diced tomatoes, vegetable broth, dried thyme, smoked paprika, salt, and black pepper. Simmer for 10 minutes.

6. Combine cooked pasta with the black-eyed pea mixture. Transfer to the greased baking dish.

7. Top with grated vegan cheese, if using.

8. Bake in the oven for 20-25 minutes or until bubbly and golden brown.

9. Garnish it with chopped fresh parsley before serving.

Nutritional Value: Calories: 250 kcal Carbohydrates: 35g Protein: 10g Fat: 8gFiber: 8g

Smoky Chicken Burrito Bowls

Prep Time: 15 minutes **Cooking time**: 30 minutes **Servings:** 4

Ingredients:

- 1 package (14 oz) vegan chicken substitute, diced
- 1 bell pepper, diced
- 1 onion, finely chopped
- 1 cup cooked rice
- 1 cup black beans, cooked
- 1 cup corn kernels, cooked
- 1 avocado, sliced
- 1/4 cup salsa
- 1/4 cup vegan sour cream
- 1 tablespoon olive oil
- 1 teaspoon smoked paprika
- 1 teaspoon ground cumin
- Salt, to taste
- Black pepper, to taste
- Fresh cilantro, chopped, for garnish

Preparation Methods:

1. Heat the olive oil in a large skillet over medium heat. Add diced vegan chicken substitute, bell pepper, and finely chopped onion. Cook until lightly browned.

2. Stir in cooked rice, black beans, and corn kernels. Season with smoked paprika, ground cumin, salt, and black pepper. Cook for another 5 minutes.

3. Serve the burrito bowl mixture in individual bowls.

4. Top each bowl with sliced avocado, salsa, and vegan sour cream.

5. Garnish with chopped fresh cilantro before serving.

Nutritional Value: Calories: 400 kcal Carbohydrates: 40g Protein:15g Fat: 20 Fiber 10g

One Pot Cheesy Black Bean Enchiladas

Prep Time: 20 minutes **Cooking time**: 30 minutes **Servings:** 4

Ingredients:

- 8 corn tortillas
- 1 can of (14 oz) black beans, drained and rinsed
- 1 can (14 oz) diced tomatoes
- 1 bell pepper, diced
- 1 onion, finely chopped
- 2 cloves garlic, minced
- 1 cup vegan cheese, shredded
- 1 cup enchilada sauce
- 1 tablespoon olive oil
- 1 teaspoon ground cumin
- 1 teaspoon chilli powder
- Salt, to taste
- Black pepper, to taste
- Fresh cilantro, chopped, for garnish
- Vegan sour cream for serving (optional)

Preparation Methods:

1. Preheat the oven to 375°F (190°C). Grease a baking dish.

2. heat the olive oil over medium heat in a big skillet. Add finely chopped onion and minced garlic, and cook until softened.

3. Add diced bell pepper to the skillet. Cook for 5 minutes.

4. Stir in drained and rinsed black beans, diced tomatoes, ground cumin, chilli powder, salt, and black pepper. Cook for another 5 minutes.

5. Spread a thin layer of enchilada sauce on the bottom of the greased baking dish.

6. Fill each corn tortilla with the black bean mixture and a sprinkle of vegan cheese. Roll up and place the seam-side down in the baking dish.

7. Pour the remaining enchilada sauce over the filled tortillas. Sprinkle with the remaining vegan cheese.

8. Bake in the oven for 20-25 minutes or until the cheese is melts and bubbly.

9. Garnish with chopped fresh cilantro before serving. Serve with vegan sour cream if desired.

Nutritional Value: Calories: 350 kcal Carbohydrates 40g Protein: 15g Fat: 15g Fiber: 10g

Thai Yellow Curry

Prep Time: 20 minutes **Cooking time**: 30 minutes **Servings:** 4

Ingredients:

- 1 can (14 oz) coconut milk
- 2 tablespoons Thai yellow curry paste
- 1 onion, thinly sliced
- 2 cloves garlic, minced
- 1 bell pepper, thinly sliced
- 1 zucchini, sliced
- 1 cup broccoli florets
- 1 cup diced tofu
- 1 tablespoon soy sauce
- 1 tablespoon brown sugar
- 1 tablespoon lime juice
- Fresh cilantro, chopped, for garnish
- Cooked rice for serving

Preparation Methods:

1. Heat coconut milk over medium heat in a large skillet or pot. Stir in Thai yellow curry paste until well combined.

2. Add thinly sliced onion and minced garlic to the skillet. Cook until softened.

3. Add thinly sliced bell pepper, sliced zucchini, broccoli florets, and diced tofu to the skillet. Cook until vegetables are tender.

4. Stir in soy sauce, brown sugar, and lime juice. Simmer for 5-10 minutes, stirring occasionally.

5. Serve hot cooked rice garnished with chopped fresh cilantro.

Nutritional Value: Calories: 300 kcal (excluding rice) Carbohydrates: 15g Protein: 10g Fat: 20g Fiber: 5g

Cheesy Gnocchi Traybake

Prep Time: 15 minutes **Cooking time**: 30 minutes **Servings:** 4

Ingredients:

- 1 package (16 oz) potato gnocchi
- 1 cup cherry tomatoes, halved
- 1 bell pepper, diced
- 1 onion, diced
- 2 cloves garlic, minced
- 1 cup spinach leaves
- 1 cup marinara sauce
- 1/2 cup vegan cheese, shredded
- 1 tablespoon olive oil
- Salt, to taste
- Black pepper, to taste
- Fresh basil, chopped, for garnish (optional)

Preparation Methods:

1. Preheat the oven to 400°F (200°C). Grease a baking dish.

2. In a large bowl, toss potato gnocchi, halved cherry tomatoes, diced bell pepper, diced onion, minced garlic, and spinach leaves with olive oil. Season with salt and black pepper.

3. Spread the gnocchi mixture evenly in the greased baking dish.

4. Pour marinara sauce over the gnocchi mixture.

5. Sprinkle shredded vegan cheese on top.

6. Bake in the preheated oven for 25-30 minutes or until the gnocchi is cooked and the cheese is melted and bubbly.

7. Garnish with chopped fresh basil before serving.

Nutritional Value: Calories: 350 kcal Carbohydrates: 50g Protein: 8g Fat: 12g Fiber: 6g

Caramelized Onion Yellow Rice with Lentils
Prep Time: 10 minutes **Cooking time**: 30 minutes **Servings:** 4

Ingredients:

- 1 cup basmati rice
- 1/2 cup lentils (any variety), rinsed
- 2 cups vegetable broth
- 2 onions, thinly sliced
- 2 tablespoons olive oil
- 1 teaspoon ground turmeric
- 1/2 teaspoon ground cumin
- Salt, to taste
- Black pepper, to taste
- Fresh parsley, chopped, for garnish (optional)

Preparation Methods:

1. heat the olive oil over medium heat in a large skillet. Add thinly sliced onions and cook until caramelized, stirring occasionally, about 20-25 minutes.

2. in a separate pot, combine basmati rice, rinsed lentils, vegetable broth, ground turmeric, ground cumin, salt, and black pepper. Bring to a boil, then reduce heat and simmer for 15-20 minutes or until rice and lentils are cooked and liquid is absorbed.

3. Once the rice and lentils are cooked, fluff with a fork and gently fold in the caramelized onions.

4. Serve it hot, garnished with chopped fresh parsley if desired.

Nutritional Value: Calories: 300 kcal
Carbohydrates: 50g Protein: 10g Fat: 8g
Fiber: 8g

Vegetable Dhansak

Prep Time: 20 minutes **Cooking time**: 40 minutes **Servings: 6**

Ingredients:

- 1 cup red lentils, rinsed
- 3 cups vegetable broth
- 2 onions, finely chopped
- 2 cloves garlic, minced
- 1 tablespoon ginger, grated
- 2 carrots, diced
- 2 potatoes, diced
- 1 cup diced butternut squash
- 1 cup diced eggplant
- 1 bell pepper, diced
- 1 can (14 oz) diced tomatoes
- 2 tablespoons curry powder
- 1 teaspoon ground turmeric
- 1 teaspoon ground cumin
- Salt, to taste
- Black pepper, to taste
- Fresh cilantro, chopped, for garnish

Preparation Methods:

1. combine rinsed red lentils and vegetable broth in a large pot. Bring to a boil, then reduce heat and simmer for 15-20 minutes or until lentils are cooked and mushy.

2. In a separate skillet, heat olive oil over medium heat. Add finely chopped onions, minced garlic, and grated ginger. Cook until onions are translucent.

3. Add diced carrots, potatoes, butternut squash, eggplant, and bell pepper to the skillet. Cook for 5-7 minutes or until vegetables are slightly soft.

4. Stir in diced tomatoes, curry powder, turmeric, cumin, salt, and black pepper. Cook for another 5 minutes.

5. Combine the cooked lentils with the vegetable mixture. Simmer it for 10-15 minutes to allow the flavours to meld together.

6. Serve it hot, garnished with chopped fresh cilantro.

Nutritional Value: Calories: 250 kcal
Carbohydrates: 40g Protein: 10g Fat: 5g
Fiber: 10g

Easy Mushroom Stroganoff

Prep Time: 10 minutes **Cooking time**: 20 minutes **Servings:** 4

Ingredients:

- 8 oz pasta of your choice
- 2 cups mushrooms, sliced
- 1 onion, finely chopped
- 2 cloves garlic, minced
- 1 cup vegetable broth
- 1/2 cup vegan sour cream
- 2 tablespoons all-purpose flour
- 2 tablespoons olive oil
- 1 tablespoon soy sauce
- 1 teaspoon Dijon mustard
- Salt, to taste
- Black pepper, to taste
- Fresh parsley, chopped, for garnish

Preparation Methods:

1. Cook pasta according to package instructions. Drain and set aside.

2. heat the olive oil over medium heat in a large skillet. Add finely chopped onion and minced garlic, and cook until softened.

3. Add sliced mushrooms to the skillet. Cook it until the mushrooms are tender and browned.

4. Stir in all-purpose flour and cook for 1-2 minutes to remove the raw flour taste.

5. Gradually pour in vegetable broth, stirring constantly to prevent lumps from forming.

6. Add vegan sour cream, soy sauce, Dijon mustard, salt, and black pepper. Stir until well combined.

7. Simmer for 5-7 minutes or until the sauce has thickened.

8. Serve hot cooked pasta garnished with chopped fresh parsley.

Nutritional Value: Calories: 300 kcal (excluding pasta) Carbohydrates: 20g Protein: 8g Fat: 15g Fiber: 5g

Air Fryer Jacket Potato Boats with Harissa Beans

Prep Time: 10 minutes **Cooking time**: 30 minutes **Servings:** 4

Ingredients:

- 4 large baking potatoes
- 1 can (14 oz) mixed beans, drained and rinsed
- 2 tablespoons harissa paste
- 2 tablespoons olive oil
- Salt, to taste
- Black pepper, to taste
- Fresh parsley, chopped, for garnish

Preparation Methods:

1. Preheat the air fryer to 400°F (200°C).

2. Wash the baking potatoes and pat them dry. Cut each potato in half lengthwise to create boat shapes.

3. Scoop out some of the flesh from each potato half to create a hollow cavity.

4. Mix the mixed beans, harissa paste, olive oil, salt, and black pepper in a bowl.

5. Spoon the bean mixture into the hollowed-out cavities of the potato boats.

6. Place the filled potato boats into the air fryer basket.

7. Air fry for 25-30 minutes or until the potatoes are well cooked and crispy outside.

8. Garnish it with chopped fresh parsley before serving.

Nutritional Value: Calories: 250 kcal Carbohydrates: 40g Protein: 8g Fat: 5g Fiber: 8g

Jerk Tofu with Rice & Peas

Prep Time: 15 minutes **Cooking time:** 30 minutes **Servings:** 4

Ingredients:

- 1 block (14 oz) tofu, pressed and sliced
- 2 cups cooked rice
- 1 can (14 oz) peas, drained
- 1 onion, finely chopped
- 2 cloves garlic, minced
- 2 tablespoons jerk seasoning
- 2 tablespoons olive oil
- 1 tablespoon soy sauce
- 1 tablespoon brown sugar
- Salt, to taste
- Black pepper, to taste
- Fresh cilantro, chopped, for garnish

Preparation Methods:

1. Mix jerk seasoning, olive oil, soy sauce, brown sugar, salt, and black pepper in a bowl.

2. Marinate the sliced tofu in the jerk seasoning mixture for at least 15 minutes.

3. Heat the olive oil in a large skillet over medium heat. Add finely chopped onion and minced garlic, and cook until softened.

4. Add marinated tofu slices to the skillet. Cook until browned on both sides.

5. Stir in cooked rice and drained peas. Cook until heated through.

6. Serve it hot, garnished with chopped fresh cilantro.

Nutritional Value: Calories: 300 kcal Carbohydrates: 35gProtein: 15g Fat: 10g Fiber: 5g

Miso Greens & Gnocchi

Prep Time: 10 minutes **Cooking time**: 20 minutes **Servings:** 4

Ingredients:

- 1 package (16 oz) potato gnocchi
- 4 cups mixed greens (such as spinach, kale, Swiss chard), chopped
- 2 tablespoons miso paste
- 2 cloves garlic, minced
- 2 tablespoons olive oil
- 1 tablespoon soy sauce
- 1 tablespoon rice vinegar
- Salt, to taste
- Black pepper, to taste
- Sesame seeds, for garnish (optional)

Preparation Methods:

1. Cook potato gnocchi according to package instructions. Drain and set aside.

2. heat the olive oil over medium heat in a large skillet. Add minced garlic and cook until it is fragrant.

3. Stir in chopped mixed greens and cook until wilted.

4. whisk together miso paste, soy sauce, and rice vinegar in a small bowl.

5. Pour the miso mixture over the cooked greens and stir to combine.

6. Add cooked gnocchi to the skillet and toss until coated in the miso sauce.

7. Cook for another 2-3 minutes, until heated through.

8. Serve hot, garnished with sesame seeds if desired.

Nutritional Value: Calories: 250 kcal Carbohydrates: 35g Protein: 5g Fat:10g Fiber: 5g

Chestnut, Mushroom & Red Wine Pithivier

Prep Time: 30 minutes **Cooking time**: 40 minutes **Servings:** 4

Ingredients:

- 1 package (16 oz) puff pastry, thawed
- 1 cup chestnuts, chopped
- 2 cups mushrooms, sliced
- 1 onion, finely chopped
- 2 cloves garlic, minced
- 1/2 cup red wine
- 2 tablespoons olive oil
- 1 tablespoon all-purpose flour
- 1 tablespoon fresh thyme leaves
- Salt, to taste
- Black pepper, to taste
- Vegan egg wash (mixture of plant-based milk and maple syrup) for brushing

Preparation Methods:

1. Preheat the oven to 375°F (190°C). Line a baking sheet with parchment paper.

2. Heat the olive oil in a large skillet over medium heat. Add finely chopped onion and minced garlic, and cook until softened.

3. Add chopped chestnuts and sliced mushrooms to the skillet. Cook until mushrooms are tender.

4. Stir in all-purpose flour and cook for 1-2 minutes to remove the raw flour taste.

5. Pour in red wine and fresh thyme leaves. Cook it until the liquid has reduced and thickened.

6. Roll out the puff pastry and cut into 8 equal squares.

7. Divide the mushroom mixture among 4 of the pastry squares, leaving a border around the edges.

8. Place the remaining pastry squares on top of the filled ones, pressing the edges to seal.

9. Use a fork to crimp the edges of the pastry.

10. Brush the tops of the pastry with vegan egg wash.

11. Bake in the oven for 20-25 minutes or until the pastry is golden brown and crispy.

12. Serve hot.

Nutritional Value: Calories: 400 kcal Carbohydrates: 30g Protein: 5g Fat: 25g Fiber: 5g

Ultimate Roast Potatoes

Prep Time: 15 minutes **Cooking time:** 45 minutes **Servings:** 4

Ingredients:

- 4 large potatoes, washed and diced
- 2 tablespoons olive oil
- 1 teaspoon garlic powder
- 1 teaspoon paprika
- Salt, to taste
- Black pepper, to taste
- Fresh rosemary, chopped, for garnish (optional)

Preparation Methods:

1. Preheat the oven to 425°F (220°C). Line a baking sheet with a parchment paper.

2. toss diced potatoes with olive oil, garlic powder, paprika, salt, and black pepper until evenly coated in a large bowl.

3. Arrange the seasoned potatoes in a single layer on the prepared baking sheet.

4. Roast in the oven for 40-45 minutes or until golden brown and crispy, flipping halfway through.

5. Garnish with chopped fresh rosemary before serving.

Nutritional Value: Calories: 200 kcal Carbohydrates: 30g Protein: 3g Fat: 8g Fiber: 4g

Creamy Tahini Kale Salad

Prep Time: 10 minutes **Cooking time**: 0 minutes **Servings:** 4

Ingredients:

- 4 cups kale, chopped
- 2 tablespoons tahini
- 2 tablespoons lemon juice
- 1 tablespoon olive oil
- 1 tablespoon maple syrup
- 1 clove garlic, minced
- Salt, to taste
- Black pepper, to taste
- Sesame seeds, for garnish (optional)

Preparation Methods:

1. In a large bowl, massage chopped kale with tahini, lemon juice, olive oil, maple syrup, minced garlic, salt, and black pepper until the kale is well-coated and tender.

2. Serve chilled, garnished with sesame seeds if desired.

Nutritional Value: Calories: 150 kcal Carbohydrates: 10g Protein: 5g Fat:10g Fiber: 3g

Herby Quinoa Salad with Pomegranate and 'Feta'

Prep Time: 15 minutes **Cooking time:** 15 minutes **Servings:** 4

Ingredients:

- 1 cup quinoa, rinsed
- 1/2 cup vegan 'feta' cheese, crumbled
- 1/4 cup fresh mint leaves, chopped
- 1/4 cup fresh parsley leaves, chopped

- 2 cups water or vegetable broth
- 1 cup pomegranate arils

- 2 tablespoons olive oil
- 2 tablespoons lemon juice
- Salt, to taste
- Black pepper, to taste

Preparation Methods:

1. combine quinoa and water or vegetable broth in a medium saucepan. Please bring it to a boil, then reduce heat and simmer the quinoa for 15 minutes or until it is cooked and the liquid is absorbed.

2. Fluff the cooked quinoa with a fork and transfer to a large mixing bowl.

3. Add pomegranate arils, crumbled vegan 'feta' cheese, chopped mint, chopped parsley, olive oil, lemon juice, salt, and black pepper to the quinoa. Toss until well combined.

4. Serve chilled or at room temperature.

Nutritional Value: Calories: 250 kcal Carbohydrates: 30g Protein: 6g Fat: 12g Fiber: 4g

Salsa

Prep Time: 10 minutes **Cooking time**: 0 minutes **Servings:** 2 cups

Ingredients:

- 4 ripe tomatoes, diced
- 1/2 onion, finely chopped
- 1 jalapeno pepper, seeded and finely chopped
- ¼ cup fresh cilantro chopped
- 2 tablespoons lime juice
- Black pepper, to taste

Preparation Methods:

1. Mix diced tomatoes, finely chopped onion, jalapeno pepper, cilantro, lime juice, salt, and black pepper in a medium bowl.

2. Blend well until all ingredients are evenly distributed.

3. Adjust seasoning to taste.

4. Serve immediately or refrigerate for at least 30 minutes to allow flavours to meld. **Nutritional Value:** Calories: 20 kcal (2 tablespoons) Carbohydrates: 5g Protein: 1g Fat: 0g Fiber: 1g

Guacamole

Prep Time: 10 minutes **Cooking time:** 0 minutes **Servings:** 2 cups

Ingredients:

- 2 ripe avocados, peeled, pitted, and mashed
- 1/2 onion, finely chopped
- 1 tomato, diced
- 1 jalapeno pepper, seeded and cut into small pieces
- 1/4 cup fresh cilantro, chopped
- 2 tablespoons lime juice
- Salt, to taste
- Black pepper, to taste

Preparation Methods:

1. Mix mashed avocados, finely chopped onion, diced tomato, jalapeno pepper, chopped cilantro, lime juice, salt, and black pepper in a medium bowl.

2. Blend very well until all ingredients are evenly combined.

3. Adjust seasoning to taste.

4. Serve immediately or refrigerate for at least 30 minutes to allow flavours to meld.

Nutritional Value: Calories: 50 kcal (2 tablespoons) Carbohydrates: 3g Protein: 1g Fat: 4g Fiber: 2g

Fast & Leafy Oriental Wraps

Prep Time: 15 minutes **Cooking time:** 0 minutes **Servings:** 4 wraps

Ingredients:

- 4 large lettuce leaves (such as romaine or butterhead)
- 1 cup cooked quinoa or rice noodles
- 1 cup shredded carrots
- 1 cup shredded red cabbage
- 1/2 cup sliced cucumber
- 1/4 cup fresh cilantro leaves
- 1/4 cup chopped peanuts or cashews
- 2 tablespoons soy sauce
- 1 tablespoon rice vinegar
- 1 tablespoon sesame oil
- 1 teaspoon grated ginger
- 1 teaspoon Sriracha sauce (optional)

Preparation Methods:

1. In a small bowl, whisk together soy sauce, rice vinegar, sesame oil, grated ginger, and Sriracha sauce (if using) to make the dressing.

2. Lay out the large lettuce leaves on a flat surface.

3. Divide cooked quinoa or rice noodles evenly among the lettuce leaves.

4. Top each lettuce leaf with shredded carrots, red cabbage, sliced cucumber, fresh cilantro leaves, and chopped peanuts or cashews.

5. Drizzle the prepared dressing over the fillings.

6. Roll up the lettuce leaves tightly to form wraps.

7. Serve immediately.

Nutritional Value: Calories: 150 kcal Carbohydrates: 15g Protein: 5g Fat: 8g Fiber: 5g

Fennel and Rocket Salad

Prep Time: 10 minutes **Cooking time**: 0 minutes **Servings:** 4

Ingredients:

- 4 cups of rocket (arugula), washed and dried
- 1 large fennel bulb, thinly sliced
- 1/4 cup walnuts, chopped
- 1/4 cup dried cranberries
- 2 tablespoons lemon juice
- 2 tablespoons olive oil
- Salt, to taste
- Black pepper, to taste

Preparation Methods:

1. combine rocket, thinly sliced fennel bulb, chopped walnuts, and dried cranberries in a large bowl.

2. whisk together lemon juice, olive oil, salt, and black pepper in a small bowl to make the dressing.

3. Pour the dressing over the salad ingredients and toss until well combined.

4. Serve immediately.

Nutritional Value: Calories: 150 kcal Carbohydrates:10g Protein: 3g Fat: 12g Fiber: 3g

Aubergine Boats

Prep Time: 15 minutes **Cooking time**: 30 minutes **Servings:** 4

Ingredients:

- 2 large aubergines (eggplants)
- 1 cup cooked quinoa

- 1 can (14 oz) chickpeas, drained and rinsed
- 1 bell pepper, diced
- 1 onion, diced

- 2 cloves garlic, minced
- 1 teaspoon ground cumin
- 1 teaspoon paprika
- 1/2 teaspoon ground coriander
- Salt, to taste
- Black pepper, to taste
- Fresh parsley, chopped, for garnish (optional)

Preparation Methods:

1. Preheat the oven to 400°F (200°C). Line a baking sheet with a parchment paper.

2. Cut each aubergine in half lengthwise. Mark traverses marks on the flesh, careful not to cut through the skin.

3. Place the aubergine halves on the prepared baking sheet and cut them side up.

4. heat the olive oil over medium heat in a big skillet. Add diced onion and minced garlic, and cook until it is soft.

5. Add diced bell pepper, cooked quinoa, drained chickpeas, ground cumin, paprika, coriander, salt, and black pepper to the skillet. Cook it for 5-7 minutes or until heated through.

6. Spoon the quinoa mixture into the hollowed-out cavities of the aubergine halves.

7. Bake in the oven for 25-30 minutes or until the aubergines are tender.

8. Garnish it with chopped fresh parsley before serving.

Nutritional Value: Calories: 250 kcal Carbohydrates: 40g Protein: 10g Fat: 5g Fiber:10g

Warm Beetroot & Quinoa Tabbouleh
Prep Time: 15 minutes **Cooking time**: 15 minutes **Servings:** 4

Ingredients:

- 1 cup quinoa, rinsed
- 2 cups water or vegetable broth
- 2 cups cooked beetroots, diced
- 1 cucumber, diced
- 1/2 cup fresh parsley, chopped
- 1/4 cup fresh mint leaves, chopped
- 1/4 cup lemon juice
- 2 tablespoons olive oil
- Salt, to taste
- Black pepper, to taste

Preparation Methods:

1. combine quinoa and water or vegetable broth in a medium saucepan. Please bring it to a boil, then reduce the heat and simmer for 15 minutes or until the quinoa is cooked and liquid is absorbed.

2. Fluff the cooked quinoa with a fork and transfer to a large mixing bowl.

3. Add diced cooked beetroots, cucumber, chopped fresh parsley, chopped fresh mint leaves, lemon juice, olive oil, salt, and black pepper to the quinoa. Toss until well combined.

4. Serve warm or at room temperature.

Nutritional Value: Calories: 200 kcal Carbohydrates: 30g Protein: 6g Fat: 8g Fiber: 5g

Pasta with Aubergine & Artichokes
Prep Time: 15 minutes **Cooking time**: 20 minutes **Servings:** 4

Ingredients:

- 8 oz pasta of your choice
- 1 large aubergine (eggplant), diced
- 1 can of (14 oz) artichoke hearts, drained and quartered
- 2 cloves garlic, minced
- 1/4 cup fresh basil leaves, chopped
- 2 tablespoons olive oil
- Salt, to taste
- Black pepper, to taste
- Vegan parmesan cheese for garnish (optional)

Preparation Methods:

1. Cook the pasta according to the package instructions. Drain and set aside.

2. heat the olive oil over medium heat in a large skillet. Add diced aubergine and minced garlic, and cook until softened.

3. Add drained and quartered artichoke hearts to the skillet. Cook for 5-7 minutes or until heated through.

4. Stir in cooked pasta and chopped fresh basil leaves. Toss until well combined.

5. Season with black pepper and salt to taste.

6. Serve hot, garnished with vegan parmesan cheese if desired.

Nutritional Value: Calories: 300 kcal Carbohydrates: 40g Protein: 8g Fat: 10g Fiber: 6g

Spicy Seitan Sausage
Prep Time: 15 minutes **Cooking time**: 30 minutes **Servings:** 8 sausages

Ingredients:

- 2 cups vital wheat gluten

- 1/4 cup nutritional yeast
- 2 tablespoons smoked paprika
- 1 tablespoon fennel seeds

- 1 teaspoon garlic powder
- 1 teaspoon onion powder
- 1 teaspoon ground black pepper
- 1 cup vegetable broth
- 1/4 cup soy sauce
- 2 tablespoons olive oil
- 2 cloves garlic, minced
- 1 tablespoon tomato paste
- 1 tablespoon sriracha sauce

Preparation Methods:

1. In a large mixing bowl, combine vital wheat gluten, nutritional yeast, smoked paprika, fennel seeds, garlic powder, onion powder, and ground black pepper.

2. whisk together vegetable broth, soy sauce, olive oil, minced garlic, tomato paste, and sriracha sauce in a separate bowl.

3. Mix the wet ingredients into the dry ingredients until a dough forms.

4. Divide the dough into 8 equal portions and shape each portion into a sausage shape.

5. Wrap each sausage in aluminium foil and steam for 20 minutes.

6. Once steamed, unwrap the sausages and grill or pan-fry them until browned on all sides.

7. Serve it hot.

Nutritional Value: Calories: 150 kcal Carbohydrates: 5g Protein: 20g Fat: 5g Fiber: 2g

Squash & Orange Arancini

Prep Time: 30 minutes **Cooking time:** 30 minutes **Servings:** 16 arancini

Ingredients:

- 2 cups risotto rice
- 4 cups vegetable broth
- 1 small butternut squash, peeled and diced
- Zest of 1 orange
- Juice of 1 orange
- 1/2 cup nutritional yeast
- 1/4 cup vegan parmesan cheese
- Salt, to taste
- Black pepper, to taste
- 1 cup breadcrumbs (use gluten-free breadcrumbs if needed)
- Olive oil for frying

Preparation Methods:

1. In a large pot, bring vegetable broth to a boil. Add the risotto rice and diced butternut squash. Reduce heat to low, cover, and simmer for about 20 minutes or until the rice is cooked and squash is tender.

2. Once cooked, stir in orange zest, orange juice, nutritional yeast, vegan parmesan cheese, salt, and black pepper. Mix until well combined.

3. Allow the mixture to cool slightly. Then, shape a spoonful of the mixture into small balls.

4. Roll each ball in breadcrumbs until evenly coated.

5. Heat the olive oil in a big skillet over medium heat. Fry the arancini in batches until golden brown and crispy on all sides.

6. Remove from the skillet and place on a paper towel-lined plate to drain excess oil.

7. Serve hot as a starter or appetizer.

Nutritional Value: Calories: 150 kcal Carbohydrates: 25g Protein: 3g Fat: 4g Fiber: 3g

Thai Coconut & Lentil Soup
Prep Time: 15 minutes **Cooking time**: 30 minutes **Servings:** 4

Ingredients:

- 1 tablespoon coconut oil
- 1 onion, chopped
- 2 cloves garlic, minced
- 1 tablespoon grated ginger
- 1 tablespoon Thai red curry paste
- 1 cup red lentils, rinsed
- 4 cups vegetable broth
- 1 can (14 oz) coconut milk
- Juice of 1 lime
- Salt, to taste
- Black pepper, to taste
- Fresh cilantro, chopped, for garnish

Preparation Methods:

1. heat the coconut oil over medium heat in a large saucepan. Add grated ginger, chopped onion and minced garlic. Cook until it is softened and fragrant.

2. Stir in Thai red curry paste and cook for another minute.

3. Add rinsed red lentils and vegetable broth to the pot. Bring to a boil, then reduce heat to low, cover, and simmer for about 20 minutes or until lentils are tender.

4. Stir in coconut milk and lime juice. Simmer for another 5-10 minutes.

5. Season it with black pepper and salt to taste.

6. Serve it hot, garnished with chopped fresh cilantro.

Nutritional Value: Calories: 300 kcal Carbohydrates: 30g Protein: 10g Fat: 15g Fiber: 10g

Squash & Ginger Pakoras with Watercress Raita

Prep Time: 20 minutes **cooking time**: 20 minutes **Servings:** 12 pakoras

Ingredients:

- 2 cups chickpea flour
- 1 cup water
- 1 cup grated butternut squash
- 2 tablespoons grated ginger
- 1 teaspoon ground cumin
- 1 teaspoon ground coriander
- 1 teaspoon turmeric
- 1/2 teaspoon cayenne pepper (optional)
- Salt, to taste
- Vegetable oil for frying
- 1 cup watercress leaves
- 1 cup vegan yoghurt
- 1 tablespoon lemon juice
- Salt, to taste
- Black pepper, to taste

Preparation Methods:

1. In a large mixing bowl, combine chickpea flour, water, grated butternut squash, grated ginger, ground cumin, ground coriander, turmeric, cayenne pepper (if using), and salt. Mix until a thick batter forms.

2. Heat vegetable oil over medium-high heat in a deep skillet or frying pan.

3. Drop a spoonful of the batter into the hot oil and fry until golden brown and crispy on all sides.

4. Remove the pakoras from the oil and place on a paper towel-lined plate to drain excess oil.

5. In a separate bowl, combine watercress leaves, vegan yoghurt, lemon juice, salt, and black pepper to make the raita.

6. Serve the hot pakoras with the watercress raita on the side.

Nutritional Value: Calories: 100 kcal Carbohydrates: 15g Protein: 5g Fat: 3g Fiber: 3g

Spinach White Bean Soup

Prep Time:15 minutes **Cooking time**: 30 minutes **Servings:** 4

Ingredients:

- 1 tablespoon olive oil
- 1 onion, chopped
- 2 cloves garlic, minced
- 4 cups vegetable broth
- 1 can (14 oz) white beans, drained and rinsed
- 4 cups fresh spinach leaves
- 1 teaspoon dried thyme
- Salt, to taste

- Black pepper, to taste
- Lemon wedges for serving

Preparation Methods:

1. heat the olive oil over medium heat in a large saucepan. Add chopped onion and minced garlic. Cook until softened and fragrant.

2. Add vegetable broth to the pot and bring to a simmer.

3. Stir in white beans, fresh spinach leaves, and dried thyme. Simmer for 15-20 minutes or until spinach wilts and flavours are well combined.

4. Season with salt and black pepper to taste.

5. Serve hot, with lemon wedges on the side for squeezing over the soup.

Nutritional Value: Calories: 150 kcal Carbohydrates: 20g Protein: 8g Fat: 3g Fiber: 6g

Salmorejo Chilled Soup

Prep Time:10 minutes **Cooking time:** 0 minutes **Servings:** 4

Ingredients:

- 4 ripe tomatoes, chopped
- 1 cucumber, peeled and chopped
- 1 red bell pepper, seeded and chopped
- 2 cloves garlic, minced
- 1/4 cup extra virgin olive oil
- 2 tablespoons red wine vinegar
- 1/2 teaspoon salt
- 1/4 teaspoon black pepper
- 1 cup stale bread, torn into pieces (optional)
- Hard-boiled eggs and chopped fresh parsley for garnish (optional)

Preparation Methods:

1. combine chopped tomatoes, chopped cucumber, chopped red bell pepper, minced garlic, extra virgin olive oil, red wine vinegar, salt, and black pepper in a blender.

2. Blend until smooth and creamy.

3. Using stale bread, add cornbread pieces to the blender and blend until well incorporated.

4. Transfer the soup to a large bowl or container and refrigerate for at least 1 hour to chill.

5. Serve the chilled soup garnished with sliced hard-boiled eggs and chopped fresh parsley, if desired.

Nutritional Value: Calories: 150 kcal
Carbohydrates: 10g Protein: 3g Fat: 10g
Fiber: 3g

Spicy Black Bean Soup

Prep Time: 15 minutes **Cooking time**: 30 minutes **Servings:** 4

Ingredients:

- 2 tablespoons olive oil
- 1 onion, chopped
- 2 cloves garlic, minced
- 1 red bell pepper, diced
- 2 teaspoons ground cumin
- 1 teaspoon chilli powder
- 1/2 teaspoon smoked paprika
- 2 cans (14 oz each) of black beans, drained and rinsed
- 4 cups vegetable broth
- 1 can (14 oz) diced tomatoes
- Juice of 1 lime
- Salt, to taste
- Black pepper, to taste
- Fresh cilantro, chopped, for garnish
- Avocado slices, for garnish (optional)

Preparation Methods:

1. Heat the olive oil in a large pot using medium heat. Add red bell pepper, chopped onion and minced garlic. Cook it until it is soft.

2. Stir in ground cumin, chilli powder, and smoked paprika. Cook for another minute.

3. Add black beans, vegetable broth, and diced tomatoes to the pot. Bring to a simmer and cook for about 20 minutes.

4. Combine the soup until it's smooth using an immersion blender. Alternatively, transfer the soup to a blender and blend in batches until smooth.

5. Stir in lime juice and season with salt and black pepper to taste.

6. If desired, Serve hot, garnished with chopped fresh cilantro and avocado slices.

Nutritional Value: Calories: 250 kcal
Carbohydrates: 40g Protein: 10g Fat: 6g
Fiber: 12g

Simple Roast Tomato Soup

Prep Time: 10 minutes **Cooking time**: 40 minutes **Servings:** 4

Ingredients:

- 2 lbs. ripe tomatoes, halved
- 2 tablespoons olive oil
- 1 onion, chopped
- 2 cloves garlic, minced
- 1 teaspoon dried basil
- 1 teaspoon dried oregano
- 4 cups vegetable broth
- Salt, to taste
- Black pepper, to taste
- Fresh basil leaves, for garnish (optional)

Preparation Methods:

1. Preheat the oven to 400°F (200°C). Put the halved tomatoes on a baking sheet cut side up. Drizzle with olive oil and season with black pepper and salt.

2. Roast tomatoes in the oven for 30-40 minutes or until softened and caramelized.

3. In a large pot, heat olive oil over medium heat. Add chopped onion and minced garlic. Cook until softened.

4. Stir in dried basil and dried oregano. Cook for another minute.

5. Add roasted tomatoes (including juices from the baking sheet) and vegetable broth to the pot. Bring to a simmer and cook for about 10 minutes.

6. Using an immersion blender, blend the soup until smooth. Alternatively, transfer the soup to a blender and blend in batches until smooth.

7. Season it with black pepper and salt to taste.

8. Serve hot, garnished with fresh basil leaves if desired.

Nutritional Value: Calories: 150 kcal Carbohydrates: 20g Protein: 4g Fat: 7g Fiber: 5g

Vegan Cauliflower Pakora

Prep Time: 20 minutes **cooking time**: 20 minutes **Servings:** 20 pakoras

Ingredients:

- 1 small cauliflower, cut into florets
- 1 cup chickpea flour
- 1/4 cup rice flour
- 1 teaspoon ground cumin
- 1 teaspoon ground coriander
- 1/2 teaspoon turmeric
- 1/2 teaspoon chilli powder
- Salt, to taste

- Water, as needed
- Vegetable oil for frying

Preparation Methods:

1. Mix chickpea flour, rice flour, ground cumin, coriander, turmeric, chili powder, and salt in a large mixing bowl.

2. Gradually add water to the dry ingredients, whisking until a smooth batter forms.

3. Dip cauliflower florets into the batter, coating evenly.

4. Heat vegetable oil using medium-high heat in a deep skillet or frying pan.

5. Fry the cauliflower florets in batches until golden brown and crispy on all sides.

6. Remove from the oil and place on a paper towel-lined plate to drain excess oil.

7. Serve it hot with your favourite dipping sauce.

Nutritional Value: Calories: 50 kcal Carbohydrates: 8g Protein: 2g Fat: 2g Fiber: 2g

Roasted Chillies Stuffed with Cashew Cheese
Prep Time: 20 minutes **Cooking time:** 20: minutes **Servings:** 12 stuffed chillies

Ingredients:

- 6 large green chillies
- 1 cup of raw cashews, soaked in water for at least 2 hours
- 2 tablespoons nutritional yeast
- 1 tablespoon lemon juice
- 1 clove garlic, minced
- Salt, to taste
- Black pepper, to taste
- Olive oil for drizzling

Preparation Methods:

1. Preheat the oven to 400°F (200°C). Line a baking sheet with parchment paper.

2. Cut each green chilli in half lengthwise and remove the seeds.

3. combine soaked cashews, nutritional yeast, lemon juice, minced garlic, salt, and black pepper in a food processor. Blend until smooth and creamy.

4. Spoon the cashew cheese mixture into each halved green chilli, filling them evenly.

5. Place the stuffed chillies on the prepared baking sheet. Drizzle with olive oil.

6. Roast in the oven for 15-20 minutes or until the chillies are soft and the cashew cheese is lightly golden.

7. Serve hot or at room temperature.

Nutritional Value: Calories: 100 kcal
Carbohydrates: 5g Protein: 3g Fat: 8g
Fiber: 2g

Tofu Caprese Salad

Prep Time: 15 minutes **Cooking time**: 0 minutes **Servings:** 4

Ingredients:

- 1 block (14 oz) firm tofu, drained and sliced
- 2 large tomatoes, sliced
- 1 cup fresh basil leaves
- 1/4 cup balsamic glaze
- 2 tablespoons extra virgin olive oil
- Salt, to taste
- Black pepper, to taste

Preparation Methods:

1. Arrange slices of tofu and tomato on a serving platter, alternating them.

2. Place fresh basil leaves on the tofu and tomato slices.

3. Sprinkle extra virgin olive and balsamic glaze oil over the salad.

4. Season with salt and black pepper to taste.

5. Serve immediately as a refreshing appetizer or light meal.

Nutritional Value: Calories: 150 kcal
Carbohydrates: 10g Protein: 10g Fat: 8g
Fiber: 2g

Pumpkin (or Squash), Lentil & Turmeric Soup

Prep Time: 15 minutes **Cooking time**: 30 minutes **Servings:** 6

Ingredients:

- 1 tablespoon olive oil
- 1 onion, chopped
- 2 cloves garlic, minced
- 2 carrots, chopped
- 2 cups diced pumpkin or squash
- 1 cup dried red lentils, rinsed
- 6 cups vegetable broth
- 1 teaspoon ground turmeric
- Salt, to taste
- Black pepper, to taste
- Fresh cilantro, chopped, for garnish (optional)

Preparation Methods:

1. heat the olive oil over medium heat in a large pot. Add chopped onion and minced garlic. Cook until softened.

2. Add chopped carrots and diced pumpkin or squash to the pot. Cook for another 5 minutes.

3. Stir in red lentils, vegetable broth, and ground turmeric. Bring to a boil, then reduce heat to low, cover, and simmer for about 20 minutes or until vegetables and lentils are tender.

4. Use an immersion blender to blend the soup until it is smooth. Alternatively, transfer the soup to a blender and blend in batches until smooth.

5. Season it with black pepper and salt to taste.

6. Serve hot, garnished with chopped fresh cilantro if desired.

Nutritional Value: Calories: 200 kcal Carbohydrates: 30g Protein:10g Fat: 4g Fiber: 8g

Green & Herby Savory Muffins

Prep Time: 15 minutes **cooking time**: 25 minutes **Servings:** 12 muffins

Ingredients:

- 2 cups all-purpose flour
- 1 tablespoon baking powder
- 1/2 teaspoon baking soda
- 1/2 teaspoon salt
- 1/4 cup nutritional yeast
- 1 cup spinach leaves, chopped
- 1/4 cup fresh basil leaves, chopped
- 1/4 cup fresh parsley, chopped
- 1/4 cup olive oil
- 1 cup unsweetened almond milk
- 2 tablespoons lemon juice
- 1 tablespoon apple cider vinegar

Preparation Methods:

1. Preheat the oven to 375°F (190°C). Grease a muffin tin or line it with muffin liners.

2. combine all-purpose flour, baking powder, baking soda, salt, and nutritional yeast in a large mixing bowl.

3. Add chopped spinach, fresh basil, and chopped parsley to the dry ingredients. Mix until well combined.

4. whisk together olive oil, unsweetened almond milk, lemon juice, and apple cider vinegar in a separate bowl.

5. Add the wet and dry ingredients to mix until just combined. Do not overmix.

6. Spoon the batter into the prepared muffin tin, filling each cup about 2/3 full.

7. Bake in the preheated oven for about 20-25 minutes or until a toothpick inserted into the centre of a muffin comes out clean.

8. Allow the muffins to cool in the tin for a few minutes before transferring them to a wire rack to cool completely.

Nutritional Value: Calories: 150 kcal Carbohydrates: 20g Protein: 5g Fat: 6g Fiber: 2g

Pistou Soup

Prep Time: 15 minutes **Cooking time**: 30 minutes **Servings:** 4

Ingredients

- 2 tablespoons olive oil
- 1 onion, chopped
- 2 cloves garlic, minced
- 2 carrots, chopped
- 2 zucchinis, chopped
- 4 cups vegetable broth
- 1 can (14 oz) diced tomatoes
- 1 can of (14 oz) cannellini beans, drained and rinsed
- 1/2 cup of small pasta (such as ditalini or small shells)
- Salt, to taste
- Black pepper, to taste
- Fresh basil leaves, for garnish (optional)

Preparation Methods:

1. Heat the olive oil in a large pot over medium heat. Add chopped onion and minced garlic. Cook until softened.

2. Add chopped carrots and chopped zucchini to the pot. Cook for another 5 minutes.

3. Stir in vegetable broth, diced tomatoes (including juices), and drained cannellini beans. Bring to a simmer.

4. Add small pasta to the pot and cook according to package instructions until al dente.

5. Season it with salt and black pepper to taste.

6. Serve hot, garnished with fresh basil leaves if desired.

Nutritional Value: Calories: 200 kcal Carbohydrates: 30g Protein: 8g Fat: 6g Fiber: 8g

Quick Vegan Cream of Watercress Soup

Prep Time: 10 minutes **Cooking time:** 20 minutes **Servings:** 4

Ingredients:

- 1 tablespoon olive oil
- 1 onion, chopped
- 2 cloves garlic, minced
- 4 cups vegetable broth
- 1 large bunch of watercress, stems removed
- 1/2 cup raw cashews, soaked in water for at least 2 hours
- Salt, to taste
- Black pepper, to taste
- Lemon wedges for serving

Preparation Methods:

1. Heat the olive oil in a large pot over medium heat. Add chopped onion and minced garlic. Cook until softened.

2. Add vegetable broth to the pot and bring to a simmer.

3. Add watercress leaves to the pot and cook for about 5 minutes or until wilted.

4. Drain the soaked cashews and add them to the pot. Cook for another 5 minutes.

5. Using an immersion blender, blend the soup until smooth. Alternatively, transfer the soup to a blender and blend in batches until smooth.

6. Season with salt and black pepper to taste.

7. Serve hot, with lemon wedges on the side for squeezing over the soup.

Nutritional Value: Calories: 150 kcal Carbohydrates:10g Protein: 5g Fat: 8g Fiber: 3g

Lemon & Blueberry Pancakes

Prep Time:10 minutes **Cooking time**:20 minutes **Servings:** 8 pancakes

Ingredients:

- 1 cup all-purpose flour
- 1 tablespoon sugar
- 1 teaspoon baking powder
- 1/2 teaspoon baking soda

- 1/4 teaspoon salt
- 1 cup almond milk (or any plant-based milk)
- 1 tablespoon lemon juice
- 1 tablespoon lemon zest

- 1 tablespoon melted vegan butter or coconut oil
- 1/2 cup blueberries (fresh or frozen)
- Maple syrup for serving

Preparation Methods:

1. whisk together all-purpose flour, sugar, baking powder, baking soda, and salt in a large mixing bowl.

2. Mix almond milk, lemon juice, lemon zest, and melted vegan butter or coconut oil in a separate bowl.

3. Mix the wet and dry ingredients and combine until combined. Do not overmix.

4. Gently fold in the blueberries.

5. Preheat a non-stick skillet or griddle over medium heat. Pour 1/4 cup of batter onto the skillet for each pancake.

6. Cook until bubbles form on the surface of the pancakes, then flip and cook until golden brown on the other side.

7. Serve hot with maple syrup.

Nutritional Value: Calories: 150 kcal Carbohydrates: 25g Protein: 3gFat: 5g Fiber: 2g

Scottish Shortbread

Prep Time: 15 minutes **Cooking time**: 25 minutes **Servings:** 12 shortbread fingers

Ingredients:

- 1 cup all-purpose flour
- 1/4 cup rice flour (or cornstarch)
- 1/2 cup vegan butter, softened
- 1/4 cup sugar
- Pinch of salt

Preparation Methods:

1. Preheat the oven to 325°F (160°C). Grease a baking tray or line it with parchment paper.

2. In a mixing bowl, cream vegan butter and sugar until light and fluffy.

3. Sift together all-purpose flour, rice flour (or cornstarch), and a pinch of salt. Gradually add this mixture to the creamed butter and sugar, mixing until a dough forms.

4. Press the dough into the prepared baking tray, smoothing the surface with a spatula or the back of a spoon.

5. Use a knife to score the dough into 12 equal-sized fingers.

6. Bake in the oven for about 20-25 minutes or until the edges are golden brown.

7. Allow the shortbread to cool in the tray for a few minutes before transferring it to a wire rack to cool completely.

Nutritional Value: Calories: 120 kcal Carbohydrates:10g Protein: 1g Fat: 8g Fiber: 0.5g

Tiramisu Tarts

Prep Time: 30 minutes **Cooking time**: 0 minutes (chilling time required) **Servings:** 6 tarts

Ingredients:

- 1 cup raw cashews, soaked in water for at least 2 hours
- 1/4 cup coconut cream
- 1/4 cup maple syrup
- 1 tablespoon instant coffee powder
- 1 teaspoon vanilla extract
- 6 vegan tart shells
- Cocoa powder for dusting

Preparation Methods:

1. Drain the soaked cashews and rinse them thoroughly.

2. combine soaked cashews, coconut cream, maple syrup, instant coffee powder, and vanilla extract in a food processor or blender. Blend until smooth and creamy.

3. Divide the cashew cream mixture among the tart shells, smoothing the surface with a spatula.

4. Refrigerate the tarts for at least 4 hours or until set.

5. Before serving, dust the top of each tart with cocoa powder.

Nutritional Value: Calories: 250 kcal Carbohydrates: 20g Protein: 5g Fat: 15g Fiber: 1g

Chocolate Mug Cake

Prep Time: 5 minutes **cooking time**: 2 minutes **Servings:** 1 mug cake

Ingredients:

- 1/4 cup all-purpose flour
- 2 tablespoons cocoa powder
- 2 tablespoons sugar
- 1/4 teaspoon baking powder
- Pinch of salt
- 3 tablespoons almond milk (or any plant-based milk)
- 1 tablespoon vegetable oil
- 1/4 teaspoon vanilla extract
- Vegan chocolate chips for topping (optional)

Preparation Methods:

1. In a microwave-safe mug, whisk together all-purpose flour, cocoa powder, sugar, baking powder, and salt until well combined.

2. Add almond milk, vegetable oil, and vanilla extract to the mug. Stir until smooth.

3. Microwave the mug cake on high for 1-2 minutes or until set.

4. Let the mug cake cool for a minute before serving.

5. Top with vegan chocolate chips if desired.

Nutritional Value: Calories: 300 kcal Carbohydrates: 40g Protein: 5g Fat:15g Fiber: 3g

Raspberry Bakewell Cake

Prep Time: 15 minutes **Cooking time**: 30 minutes **Servings:**1 cake (8 slices)

Ingredients:

- 1 cup all-purpose flour
- 1/2 cup almond flour
- 1/2 cup sugar
- 1 teaspoon baking powder
- 1/4 teaspoon salt
- 1/2 cup almond milk (or any plant-based milk)
- 1/4 cup vegetable oil
- 1 teaspoon almond extract
- 1/2 cup raspberry jam
- Sliced almonds for topping

Preparation Methods:

1. Preheat the oven to 350°F (180°C). Grease and line a round cake tin.

2. whisk together all-purpose flour, almond flour, sugar, baking powder, and salt in a large mixing bowl.

3. Add almond milk, vegetable oil, and almond extract to the dry ingredients. Stir until well combined.

4. Pour half of the batter into the prepared cake tin. Spread raspberry jam evenly over the batter.

5. Carefully spoon the remaining batter over the jam layer, spreading it to cover.

6. Sprinkle sliced almonds over the top of the cake.

7. Bake in the preheated oven for about 25-30 minutes or until a toothpick inserted into the centre comes clean.

8. Allow the cake to cool in the tin for a few minutes before transferring it to a wire rack to cool completely.

Nutritional Value: Calories: 250 kcal
Carbohydrates: 30g Protein: 4g Fat: 12g
Fiber: 2g

Easy Strawberry Galette with Vegan Whipped Cream
Prep Time: 20 minutes **Cooking time:** 25 minutes **Servings:** 6

Ingredients:

- 1 vegan pie crust (store-bought or homemade)
- 2 cups fresh strawberries, sliced
- 1/4 cup granulated sugar
- 1 tablespoon cornstarch
- 1 teaspoon vanilla extract
- 1 tablespoon almond milk (for brushing)
- 1 tablespoon coarse sugar (for sprinkling)
- Vegan whipped cream for serving

Preparation Methods:

1. Preheat the oven to 375°F (190°C).

2. mix the strawberries with granulated sugar, cornstarch, and vanilla extract in a bowl.

3. Roll out the pie crust on a baking sheet lined with parchment paper.

4. Place the strawberry mixture in the centre of the crust, leaving about a 2-inch border.

5. Fold the edges of the crust over the strawberries, pleating as necessary.

6. Brush the crust with almond milk and sprinkle with coarse sugar.

7. Bake for 25 minutes or until the crust is golden and the filling is bubbly.

8. Serve warm or at room temperature with vegan whipped cream.

Nutritional Value: Calories: 250 kcal
Carbohydrates: 38g Protein: 3g Fat:10g
Fiber: 2g

Easy Vegan Coffee & Walnut Cake
Prep Time: 15 minutes **cooking time:** 30 minutes **Servings:** 1 cake (8 slices)

Ingredients:

- 1 and 1/2 cups all-purpose flour
- 3/4 cup granulated sugar
- 1 teaspoon baking powder
- 1/2 teaspoon baking soda
- 1/2 teaspoon salt
- 1 cup strong brewed coffee (cooled)
- 1/3 cup vegetable oil

- 1 teaspoon vanilla extract
- 1/2 cup chopped walnuts

Preparation Methods:

1. Preheat the oven to 350°F (175°C). Grease and flour an 8-inch cake pan.

2. Sift flour, sugar, baking powder, baking soda, and salt in a large mixing bowl.

3. whisk together the coffee, vegetable oil, and vanilla extract in another bowl.

4. Add the wet and dry ingredients to mix until just combined.

5. Fold in the chopped walnuts.

6. Pour the batter into the prepared cake pan.

7. Bake for 30 minutes or until a toothpick inserted into the centre comes clean.

8. Let the cake cool in the pan for 10 minutes, then turn it onto a wire rack to cool completely.

Nutritional Value: Calories: 280 kcal Carbohydrates: 38g Protein: 4g Fat:14g Fiber: 1g

Roasted Pineapple with Miso & Rum
Prep Time: 10 minutes **Cooking time:**15 minutes **Servings:** 4

Ingredients:

- 1 large pineapple, peeled, cored, and cut into 8 spears
- 2 tablespoons miso paste
- 2 tablespoons dark rum
- 2 tablespoons brown sugar
- 1 teaspoon ground cinnamon

Preparation Methods:

1. Preheat the oven to 400°F (200°C).

2. Mix miso paste, dark rum, brown sugar, and cinnamon in a small bowl.

3. Arrange the pineapple spears on a baking sheet lined with parchment paper.

4. Brush the miso mixture over the pineapple spears.

5. Roast in the oven for 15 minutes, turning halfway through, until caramelized and tender.

6. Serve warm.

Nutritional Value: Calories: 180 kcal Carbohydrates: 30g Protein: 2g Fat: 3g Fiber: 3g

Almond & Pistachio Sponge

Prep Time: 15 minutes **cooking time**: 25 minutes **Servings:** 1 cake (8 slices)

Ingredients:

- 1 cup almond flour
- 1/2 cup ground pistachios
- 1/2 cup granulated sugar
- 1 teaspoon baking powder
- 1/4 teaspoon salt
- 1/2 cup plant-based milk
- 1/4 cup vegetable oil
- 1 teaspoon almond extract

Preparation Methods:

1. Preheat the oven to 350°F (175°C). Grease and line an 8-inch cake tin.

2. Mix almond flour, ground pistachios, sugar, baking powder, and salt in a bowl.

3. Stir in plant-based milk, vegetable oil, and almond extract until well combined.

4. Pour the batter into the prepared cake tin.

5. Bake for 25 minutes or until a toothpick inserted into the centre comes clean.

6. Let the cake cool in the tin for 10 minutes before transferring to a wire rack to cool completely.

Nutritional Value: Calories: 260 kcal Carbohydrates: 20g Protein: 6g Fat: 18g Fiber: 3g

Mint Chocolate Tart

Prep Time: 20 minutes **Cooking time**: No bake, chill for 2 hours **Servings:** 8

Ingredients:

- 1 and 1/2 cups crushed vegan chocolate cookies
- 1/3 cup coconut oil, melted
- 1 cup dark chocolate chips
- 1 cup canned coconut cream
- 1/4 cup agave syrup
- 1 teaspoon peppermint extract

1. Mix crushed cookies with melted coconut oil and press into the bottom and sides of a tart pan. Chill in the refrigerator to set.

2. In a saucepan, melt the chocolate chips with coconut cream over low heat, stirring until smooth.

3. Remove from heat and stir in agave syrup and peppermint extract.

Preparation Methods:

4. Pour the chocolate mixture into the chilled crust.

5. Chill in the refrigerator for at least 2 hours or until set.

6. Serve chilled.

Nutritional Value: Calories: 350 kcal Carbohydrates: 30g Protein: 3g Fat: 25g Fiber: 3g

Raspberry & White Chocolate Blondies

Prep Time: 15 minutes **cooking time**: 25 minutes **Servings:** 12 blondies

Ingredients:

- 2 cups all-purpose flour (gluten-free if needed)
- 1 tsp baking powder
- 1/2 tsp salt
- 1 cup vegan white chocolate chips
- 1/2 cup unsweetened applesauce
- 1 cup sugar substitute (like erythritol)
- 1/2 cup unsweetened almond milk
- 1/4 cup coconut oil, melted
- 1 tsp vanilla extract
- 1 cup fresh raspberries

Preparation Methods:

1. Preheat your oven to 350°F (175°C) and line a 9x9 inch baking pan with parchment paper.

2. Mix flour, baking powder, and salt in a large bowl.

3. mix applesauce, sugar substitute, almond milk, melted coconut oil, and vanilla extract in another bowl.

4. Mix the wet and dry ingredients. Fold in the white chocolate chips and raspberries gently.

5. Pour the batter into the prepared pan and spread it evenly.

6. Bake for 25 minutes or until a toothpick comes out clean.

7. Let cool before slicing into squares.

Nutritional Value: Calories: 200kcal Protein: 4g Fat: 8g Carbohydrates: 28g Fiber, 2g Sugar: 12g.

Mini Egg Cookie Traybake

Prep Time: 10 minutes **Cooking time**: 20 minutes **Servings:** 16

Ingredients:

- 2 1/2 cups all-purpose flour (gluten-free if needed)
- 1 tsp baking soda
- 1/2 tsp salt
- 1 cup vegan butter, softened
- 3/4 cup sugar substitute (like erythritol)
- 1/4 cup brown sugar substitute
- 2 tsp vanilla extract
- 1/2 cup unsweetened almond milk
- 1 cup vegan mini chocolate eggs

Preparation Methods:

1. Preheat the oven to 350°F (175°C) and grease a large baking tray or line with parchment paper.

2. Mix the flour, baking soda, and salt in a bowl.

3. In another bowl, cream the vegan butter with sugar substitutes until light and fluffy. Add vanilla extract and almond milk, mixing until well combined.

4. Gradually add the dry ingredients to the wet, mixing until a dough forms. Fold in the vegan mini chocolate eggs.

5. Press the dough evenly into the prepared tray.

6. Bake for 20 minutes or until golden brown and a toothpick comes out clean.

7. Cool in the tray before cutting into squares.

Nutritional Value: Calories: 180kcal Protein: 2g Fat: 10g Carbohydrates: 21g Fiber:1g Sugar: 10g

Classic Carrot Cake

Prep Time: 20 minutes **Cooking time**: 35 minutes **Servings:** 12

Ingredients:

- 2 cups finely grated carrots
- 1 1/2 cups all-purpose flour (gluten-free if needed)
- 1 tsp baking powder
- 1 tsp baking soda
- 1/2 tsp salt
- 2 tsp cinnamon
- 1/2 cup unsweetened applesauce
- 1 cup sugar substitute (like erythritol)
- 1/2 cup vegetable oil
- 1/4 cup unsweetened almond milk
- 1 tsp vanilla extract

- 1/2 cup chopped walnuts (optional)

Preparation Methods:

1. Preheat your oven to 350°F (175°C) and grease a 9-inch cake pan.

2. combine flour, baking powder, baking soda, salt, and cinnamon in a bowl.

3. mix applesauce, sugar substitute, vegetable oil, almond milk, and vanilla in another bowl. Stir in grated carrots.

4. Gradually mix the dry ingredients into the wet until well combined. Fold in walnuts if using.

5. Pour into the prepared pan and bake for 35 minutes or until a toothpick comes out clean.

6. Let it cool before serving.

Nutritional Value: Calories: 210kcal Protein: 2g Fat:12g Carbohydrates: 24g Fiber: 3g Sugar: 12g

Black Forest Gateau Smoothie

Prep Time: 5 minutes **Cooking time**: 0 minutes **Servings:** 2

Ingredients:

- 1 cup frozen cherries
- 1 ripe banana
- 1 tbsp cocoa powder
- 1 cup unsweetened almond milk
- 1/2 cup coconut yoghurt
- Sugar substitute to taste (optional)

Preparation Methods:

1. Place all ingredients in a blender.

2. Blend until smooth.

3. Serve immediately, optionally garnished with additional cherries or a sprinkle of cocoa powder.

Nutritional Value: Calories: 150kcal Protein: 3g Fat: 4g Carbohydrates: 26g Fiber: 5g Sugar: 14g (natural sugars from fruits).

Week 1

Day 1

- Breakfast: Lemon & Blueberry Pancakes
- Lunch: Creamy Tahini Kale Salad
- Dinner: Vegan Cauliflower Pakora with Spinach White Bean Soup
- Snack: Raspberry & White Chocolate Blondies

Day 2

- Breakfast: Porridge with Flax seeds, Berries and Banana
- Lunch: Squash & Ginger Pakoras with Watercress Raita
- Dinner: Thai Yellow Curry with Brown Rice
- Snack: Mini Egg Cookie Traybake

Day 3

- Breakfast: Chocolate Protein Chia Pudding
- Lunch: Herby Quinoa Salad with Pomegranate and 'Feta'
- Dinner: Easy Quiche with Broccoli & Sundried Tomatoes
- Snack: Almond & Pistachio Sponge

Day 4

- Breakfast: Super Green Superfruit Protein Smoothie
- Lunch: Warm Beetroot & Quinoa Tabbouleh
- Dinner: Chickpea, Sweet Potato & Tomato Curry with Baked Rice Pilaf with Squash
- Snack: Scottish Shortbread

Day 5

- Breakfast: Tofu Caprese Salad
- Lunch: Spinach White Bean Soup with Fennel and Rocket Salad
- Dinner: Super-fast Scrambled Tofu with Aubergine Boats
- Snack: Easy Vegan Coffee & Walnut Cake

Day 6

- Breakfast: Raspberry Bakewell Cake
- Lunch: Vegan Sausage Sandwich Lowdown
- Dinner: Layered Festive Roast with Vegan Gravy
- Snack: Mint Chocolate Tart

Day 7

- Breakfast: Porridge with Flax seeds, Berries and Banana

- Lunch: Quick Vegan Cream of Watercress Soup with Fast & Leafy Oriental Wraps
- Dinner: Easy Vegan Spaghetti Bolognese
- Snack: Easy Strawberry Galette with Vegan Whipped Cream

Week 2

Day 8

- Breakfast: Lemon & Blueberry Pancakes
- Lunch: Warm Beetroot & Quinoa Tabbouleh
- Dinner: One Pot Rainbow Pasta
- Snack: Chocolate Mug Cake

Day 9

- Breakfast: Porridge with Flax seeds, Berries and Banana
- Lunch: Pistou Soup with Green & Herby Savory Muffins
- Dinner: Sweet Potato, Spicy Black Beans & Guacamole
- Snack: Raspberry & White Chocolate Blondies

Day 10

- Breakfast: Tofu Caprese Salad
- Lunch: Thai Coconut & Lentil Soup with Squash & Orange Arancini
- Dinner: Vegan Cauliflower Pakora with Spinach White Bean Soup

- Snack: Scottish Shortbread

Day 11

- Breakfast: Super Green Superfruit Protein Smoothie
- Lunch: Squash & Ginger Pakoras with Watercress Raita
- Dinner: Spicy Vegan Bean Burgers with Cheesy Gnocchi Traybake
- Snack: Mini Egg Cookie Traybake

Day 12

- Breakfast: Chocolate Protein Chia Pudding
- Lunch: Herby Quinoa Salad with Pomegranate and 'Feta'
- Dinner: Chana Masala with Baked Rice Pilaf with Squash
- Snack: Almond & Pistachio Sponge

Day 13

- Breakfast: Raspberry Bakewell Cake
- Lunch: Vegan Sausage Sandwich Lowdown
- Dinner: Layered Festive Roast with Vegan Gravy
- Snack: Mint Chocolate Tart

Day 14

- Breakfast: Porridge with Flax seeds, Berries and Banana
- Lunch: Quick Vegan Cream of Watercress Soup with Fast & Leafy Oriental Wraps
- Dinner: Easy Vegan Spaghetti Bolognese
- Snack: Easy Strawberry Galette with Vegan Whipped Cream

Week 3

Day 15

- Breakfast: Lemon & Blueberry Pancakes
- Lunch: Warm Beetroot & Quinoa Tabbouleh
- Dinner: Chickpea, Sweet Potato & Tomato Curry with Basmati Rice
- Snack: Chocolate Mug Cake

Day 16

- Breakfast: Porridge with Flax seeds, Berries and Banana
- Lunch: Pistou Soup with Green & Herby Savory Muffins
- Dinner: Easy Quiche with Broccoli & Sundried Tomatoes
- Snack: Raspberry & White Chocolate Blondies

Day 17

- Breakfast: Tofu Caprese Salad

- Lunch: Thai Coconut & Lentil Soup with Squash & Orange Arancini
- Dinner: One Pot of Cheesy Black Bean Enchiladas
- Snack: Scottish Shortbread

Day 18

- Breakfast: Super Green Superfruit Protein Smoothie
- Lunch: Squash & Ginger Pakoras with Watercress Raita
- Dinner: Spicy Vegan Bean Burgers with Cheesy Gnocchi Traybake
- Snack: Mini Egg Cookie Traybake

Day 19

- Breakfast: Chocolate Protein Chia Pudding
- Lunch: Herby Quinoa Salad with Pomegranate and 'Feta'
- Dinner: Layered Festive Roast with Vegan Gravy
- Snack: Mint Chocolate Tart

Day 20

- Breakfast: Raspberry Bakewell Cake
- Lunch: Vegan Sausage Sandwich Lowdown
- Dinner: Easy Vegan Spaghetti Bolognese
- Snack: Easy Strawberry Galette with Vegan Whipped Cream

Day 21

- Breakfast: Porridge with Flax seeds, Berries and Banana
- Lunch: Quick Vegan Cream of Watercress Soup with Fast & Leafy Oriental Wraps
- Dinner: Spanish White Wine Lentils with Tortilla De Patatas
- Snack: Almond & Pistachio Spong

Week 4

Day 22

- Breakfast: Lemon & Blueberry Pancakes
- Lunch: Warm Beetroot & Quinoa Tabbouleh
- Dinner: Sweet Potato, Spicy Black Beans & Guacamole
- Snack: Chocolate Mug Cake

Day 23

- Breakfast: Porridge with Flax seeds, Berries and Banana
- Lunch: Pistou Soup with Green & Herby Savory Muffins
- Dinner: Aubergine & Green Lentil Koftas with Broccoli, Lemon & Mint Risotto
- Snack: Raspberry & White Chocolate Blondies

Day 24

- Breakfast: Tofu Caprese Salad

- Lunch: Thai Coconut & Lentil Soup with Squash & Orange Arancini
- Dinner: Multi Grain Risotto with Spinach White Bean Soup
- Snack: Scottish Shortbread

Day 25

- Breakfast: Super Green Superfruit Protein Smoothie
- Lunch: Squash & Ginger Pakoras with Watercress Raita
- Dinner: Spicy Vegan Bean Burgers with Cheesy Gnocchi Traybake
- Snack: Mini Egg Cookie Traybake

Day 26

- Breakfast: Chocolate Protein Chia Pudding
- Lunch: Herby Quinoa Salad with Pomegranate and 'Feta'
- Dinner: Quick & Easy Chana Masala with Basmati Rice
- Snack: Mint Chocolate Tart

Day 27

- Breakfast: Raspberry Bakewell Cake
- Lunch: Vegan Sausage Sandwich Lowdown
- Dinner: Easy Vegan Spaghetti Bolognese
- Snack: Easy Strawberry Galette with Vegan Whipped Cream

Day 28

- Breakfast: Porridge with Flax seeds, Berries and Banana
- Lunch: Quick Vegan Cream of Watercress Soup with Fast & Leafy Oriental Wraps
- Dinner: Layered Festive Roast with Vegan Gravy
- Snack: Almond & Pistachio Sponge

Day 29

- Breakfast: Lemon & Blueberry Pancakes
- Lunch: Warm Beetroot & Quinoa Tabbouleh
- Dinner: One Pot Rainbow Pasta
- Snack: Chocolate Mug Cake

Day 30

- Breakfast: Porridge with Flax seeds, Berries and Banana
- Lunch: Pistou Soup with Green & Herby Savory Muffins
- Dinner: Super Stuffed Tempeh Sandwich with Broccoli, Lemon & Mint Risotto
- Snack: Raspberry & White Chocolate Blondies

Produce:

- Leafy greens (spinach, kale, Swiss chard)
- Cruciferous vegetables (broccoli, cauliflower, Brussels sprouts)
- Bell peppers (red, green, yellow)
- Tomatoes
- Carrots
- Celery
- Cucumbers
- Zucchini
- Mushrooms
- Onions (red, white, yellow)
- Garlic
- Ginger
- Avocado
- Berries (strawberries, blueberries, raspberries)
- Apples
- Oranges
- Lemons
- Bananas
- Grapes
- Potatoes (sweet potatoes, Yukon gold)
- Squash (butternut squash, acorn squash)
- Fresh herbs (basil, cilantro, parsley, mint)

Grains and Legumes:

- Quinoa
- Brown rice
- Whole wheat pasta (or gluten-free alternative)
- Rolled oats
- Lentils (green, brown, red)
- Chickpeas
- Black beans
- Kidney beans
- Cannellini beans

Nuts and Seeds:

- Almonds
- Walnuts
- Pecans
- Pistachios
- Cashews
- Chia seeds
- Flaxseeds
- Hemp seeds
- Sunflower seeds

Dairy Alternatives:

- Almond milk (unsweetened)
- Soy milk (unsweetened)
- Oat milk (unsweetened)
- Coconut milk (unsweetened, canned)
- Vegan yoghurt (unsweetened)
- Vegan cheese (optional)

Plant-based Proteins:

- Tofu (extra firm)
- Tempeh
- Seitan
- Vegan sausage or burger patties (low sodium)
- Plant-based protein powder (unsweetened)

Healthy Fats and Oils:

- Extra virgin olive oil
- Coconut oil
- Avocado oil
- Flaxseed oil
  Sweeteners:
- Stevia
- Erythritol
- Monk fruit sweetener
- Agave nectar
- Maple syrup (unsweetened)
  Spices and Seasonings:
- Salt (preferably Himalayan pink salt)
- Black pepper
- Garlic powder
- Onion powder
- Paprika

- Cumin
- Turmeric
- Cinnamon
- Nutmeg
- Vanilla extract

Condiments and Sauces:

- Low-sodium soy sauce or tamari
- Balsamic vinegar
- Apple cider vinegar
- Dijon mustard
- Tomato paste (unsweetened)
- Salsa (unsweetened)
- Hot sauce (without added sugar)

Miscellaneous:

- Baking powder
- Baking soda
- Whole grain flour (all-purpose, whole wheat)
- Vegan protein bars (unsweetened)
- Dark chocolate (unsweetened, at least 70% cocoa)
- Unsweetened coconut flakes
- Nutritional yeast

Conversion Chart

Here's a comprehensive conversion chart covering common measurements used in cooking.

Volume Measurements

- 1 teaspoon (tsp) = 5 milliliters (ml)

- 1 tablespoon (tbsp) = 15 milliliters (ml)

- 1 fluid ounce (Fl oz) = 30 millilitres (ml)

- 1 cup = 240 milliliters (ml)

- 1 pint = 480 milliliters (ml)

- 1 quart = 960 milliliters (ml)

- 1 gallon = 3.8 liters (L)

Weight Measurements

- 1 ounce (oz) = 28 grams (g)

- 1 pound (lb.) = 16 ounces (oz) = 454 grams (g)

Temperature

- Celsius to Fahrenheit: °F = (°C × 9/5) + 32

- Fahrenheit to Celsius: °C = (°F - 32) × 5/9

- Common oven temperature conversions:

  - 350°F = 180°C

  - 375°F = 190°C

  - 400°F = 200°C

  - 425°F = 220°C

Common Ingredient Substitutions

- For egg replacement in baking: 1 tablespoon ground flaxseed + 3 tablespoons water (let it sit for 5 minutes) = 1 egg
- For dairy milk replacement: 1 cup almond milk, soy milk, oat milk, or coconut milk = 1 cup dairy milk
- For butter replacement: 1 cup coconut oil or vegan margarine = 1 cup butter
- For honey replacement: Equal parts agave nectar, maple syrup, or brown rice syrup = honey
- For white sugar replacement: Equal parts granulated erythritol, xylitol, or coconut sugar = white sugar

Miscellaneous

- 1 pinch = Approximately 1/16 teaspoon

- 1 dash = Approximately 1/8 teaspoon

- 1 handful = Approximately 1/2 cup

Conclusion

High levels of internal fat (fat in and around the heart, liver, and pancreas) have been implicated in causing insulin resistance. Weight loss alone has been shown to increase insulin sensitivity. Reducing calorie intake is an obvious way to lose weight, but the type of food you eat is equally important. A low-fat, plant-based diet has repeatedly been demonstrated to improve insulin sensitivity and lowering internal fat levels. Internal fat is highly responsive to dietary change and can decrease rapidly once the right changes are made.

High carbohydrate intake has long been responsible for unstable blood glucose levels, and sound evidence supports this. As a vegan, most of your carbohydrate intake is likely from whole grains, vegetables, fruits, and beans, which are all very healthy food choices. That being said, some are better choices than others. Familiarizing yourself with the glycemic index and choosing low-GI foods will help you to control your blood glucose.

Learning to prepare healthful, nutritious meals is the most important thing you can do to take control of your diabetes. This book is an effort to show that eating can still be a gratifying experience, so you need not feel constrained by your new dietary restraints. Your health is worth the time, effort, and money you put into it, and I hope this book provides clear evidence.

Overall, I encourage people newly diagnosed with diabetes to remember that it is very manageable and need not deter you from a long and worthwhile life. With the right tools and encouragement, you can take control of your health and be a champion for yourself and a future generation free of this disease. Learning to manage diabetes is a steep learning curve, but I hope that this cookbook makes it easier to understand

Encouragement for a Healthy Vegan Type 2 Diabetic Lifestyle

It would be best if you believed in yourself. Believe that you can change those eating habits that are unhealthy and very much into your way of life. Remember, moderation is the key. Sometimes, we deprive ourselves of certain foods and eat them later. If you have slip-ups, remind yourself that it is human and that eating high-fat, high-calorie, or unhealthily sweetened products is known to be addictive.

When you have an addictive personality, it is tough to break something cold turkey but remind yourself that nothing is beyond your control. Practice self-love concerning the foods you eat. If you eat something that is not good for your diabetes, and perhaps you had a little more than you should, don't beat yourself up over it. You aren't the wrong person, which doesn't mean you can't change.

Think about how long it took you to fall into the eating habits that are detrimental to your health; it was probably over several years. Changing habits takes time, and since you have committed to better yourself, every day is a new day to continue that commitment. Being diagnosed with type two diabetes while being a vegetarian or vegan is not a forbidden zone.

It is the time to reevaluate your health. If you, as a vegetarian or a vegan, were previously diagnosed with this condition, it is now your calling to improve your lifestyle by eating healthier. This isn't the end to vegetarianism or veganism because both lifestyles have many health benefits. As a vegan, you should start integrating more low-GI foods into your diet, as research shows that the more plant foods consumed, the lower the risk of developing type 2 diabetes. A vegan diet is naturally higher in fibre, and many low GI foods are high in fibre; therefore, getting the nutrients you need from a vegan meal is very easy. Remember that there are many

advantages to being vegetarian or vegan with diabetes. Plant foods are very nutrient-dense and provide a diverse range of phytonutrients.

In addition, many plant foods contain substances that help prevent and manage chronic diseases. Another plus is that a diet high in phytochemicals from plant foods acts as an antioxidant. High blood glucose levels cause more damage to body cells than low levels, and high glucose levels can also increase the rate at which the body produces free radicals compared to a person with normal glucose levels.

Free radicals can cause damage to cells, which can lead to problems such as heart disease, kidney disease, and nerve and retinal damage. Antioxidants work to neutralize free radicals and stop any damage being done to cells. In prevention of chronic diseases, research has shown that plant food antioxidants can help protect against diseases that diabetics are at a higher risk of developing, such as heart disease and certain types of cancer.

Thank You Note

Dear Reader,

Thank you for choosing 'The Latest Vegan Type 2 Diabetes Diet Cookbook for Newly Diagnosed.' It's been a labour of love crafting these delicious and nutritious recipes explicitly tailored for those navigating a vegan lifestyle while managing type 2 diabetes. Your commitment to your health inspires us, and we hope this book empowers you on your journey to better well-being. Let's embrace the power of wholesome, plant-based foods to thrive and live our best lives.

Now that you've finished reading this book, it'd mean the world to me if you did leave your honest thoughts about it on Amazon.

With gratitude,

Charlotte N. Smith

.

Made in United States
Orlando, FL
09 December 2024

55259639R00061